THE MACALLAN GREAT SCOTS QUIZ BOOK

1/91

INTRODUCTION

Scotland, in all its <u>splendid shapes and forms,</u> is the subject and indeed object of this Quiz Book.

As you pit your wits against its challenges, you will find a <u>unique source of information</u> about your favourite country within the covers.

Some of it, just a smattering, will be about our pride and joy, the Macallan — number <u>one malt whisky</u> on Speyside, Highland heartland of the <u>distiller's art</u>.

It is with the greatest pleasure that we now present the Quiz in all its <u>puzzling profusion</u>. If in the course of your mental activities, you feel the need for a little Macallan refreshment, you will of course go <u>straight to the top of the</u> glass.

Prestige Sales & Developments, 41 Haddricks Mill Road, South Gosforth, Newcastle upon Tyne, NE3 1QL.

First published 1990.

© Prestige Sales & Developments, 41 Haddricks Mill Road, South Gosforth, Newcastle upon Tyne, NE3 1QL.

Typeset by S. B. Typesetters, Byron House, Byron Street, Newcastle upon Tyne, NE2 1XH.

Made and printed in Great Britain by C.W.S. Printers, Pelaw, Gateshead, Tyne and Wear.

Questions and picture quiz were supplied by Quest N.E.

£2.99

THE MACALLAN GREAT SCOTS QUIZ

Quiz 1

1. Which Lennon and McCartney song gave Marmalade their first No. 1 Hit?
2. What was the nickname of Celtic's European Cup winning side of 1967?
3. Who won the 1990 British Open at St. Andrews?
4. Where is the home of the Scottish Opera?
5. Which BBC programme 'discovered' Sheena Easton?
6. Who journeyed to Iona in 563AD to found a Christian settlement?
7. What is the home town of singing star, Lena Zavaroni?
8. Which famous explorer has a centre named after him at Blantyre?
9. What has been the headquarters to the Clan Campbell since the 15th Century?
10. What is the official road number of the road between Ardlius and Balloch on the Western Shore of Loch Lomond?
11. What was the capital of Scotland before Edinburgh?
12. Which Scottish football captain transferred to Newcastle United in January 1990?
13. Who is generally regarded as the father of modern television?
14. Which castle was modelled on the Chateau De Coucy in France?
15. By what name is the 8th hole at Troon better known?
16. What is reputedly Edinburgh's oldest building?
17. How many streets comprise 'The Royal Mile'?
18. Who succeeded Jeremy Thorpe as Leader of the Liberal Party?
19. Which two players have won the Open at Turnberry?
20. Who designed the bridge over the Tay at Dunkeld?

Quiz 2

1. Which family built Crathes Castle?
2. Which group had a hit in 1975 with 'Pick Up The Pieces'?
3. Where was speedway staged in Edinburgh after 1977?
4. Whose home is known as the 'Palace in Culross'?
5. Whose family motto is 'Gang Warily'?
6. Who built Kilchurn Castle near Loch Awe in the 15th Century?
7. In which place did Robert Burns found his Batchelor Club?
8. The Duke of Rothesay is an Hereditary Title of which Royal Peerage?
9. What is the most westerly point on the Scottish mainland?
10. Where is the setting for Robbie Burn's poem 'Tam O'Shanter'?
11. What separates the Isle of Mull from the Argyllshire mainland?
12. What was raised by 17ft in 1859 when it became one of Glasgow's chief water supplies?
13. Which Scottish TV personality fronted 'The Media Show' and 'The Tube'?
14. During which months of the year are The Royal Family usually in residence at Balmoral?
15. Which Scottish alternative comedian appeared in the TV series 'Tutti Frutti?
16. What did the Romans call Scotland?
17. Who scored two goals against Scotland in their opening match of the 1978 World Cup?
18. To whom is comedienne, Pamela Stephenson married?
19. Which Scottish player was voted 'Player of the Year' in England in 1978?
20. Which actor played the part of Frazer in 'Dads Army'?

THE MACALLAN GREAT SCOTS QUIZ

Quiz 3

1. When was the Forth Road Bridge opened?
2. Which Edinburgh monument, opened in 1840, boasts 247 steps to the top?
3. Which was the only team Scotland defeated in the 1974 World Cup Finals?
4. Where is the home of the Earl of Haddington?
5. Which group had a hit with 'Letter from America' in 1987?
6. In which year was the first passenger steamer launched on the Clyde?
7. What is the highest mountain in Scotland?
8. Who built Dunksey Castle in 1510?
9. What is the largest of the islands of the Inner Hebrides?
10. What is the county town of Buteshire, including the Isle of Arran?
11. In which year was Robert Burns born?
12. What is the name of Scotland's largest inland loch?
13. In which castle was Princess Margaret born?
14. In which garden are there some interesting stone figures from Robbie Burn's 'Tam O' Shanter'?
15. Where is the lighthouse designed by Alan Stevenson in 1849 which is 118ft. high and has a light visible for some 17 miles?
16. In which two counties is Loch Lomond situated?
17. Which monarch died at Stirling Castle in 1124?
18. Which river runs through the 'Sma Glen' in Perthshire?
19. Who built the surviving 15th Century hall at Stirling Castle?
20. Who built the bridge at Aberfeldy which is generally regarded as his masterpiece?

Quiz 4

1. Who is the owner of Glamis Castle?
2. Who was the lead singer with 'Altered Images'?
3. Which castle on the Isle of Mull was restored from a ruined state in 1912?
4. What is the highest point on the Isle of Mull?
5. Whose home is the Chapel of Stobhall?
6. Why was the ceiling of the Chapel of the Palace of Falkland decorated in 1633?
7. Who had a hit in May 1982 with the song 'We Have a Dream'?
8. With which Shakespeare play is Glamis Castle associated?
9. What was the Perthshire town of Crieff originally called?
10. Who by-passed Stirling Castle and did not attack it until all other towns had surrendered to him?
11. Who designed Balmoral Castle?
12. Who built the original road on the south side of Loch Ness?
13. What is the most easterly point on the Scottish mainland?
14. Which memorial was unveiled by the Queen Mother at Spean Bridge in 1952?
15. Who is the main female presenter on TVAM?
16. From which Castle have the most frequently reported sightings of the Loch Ness monster occurred?
17. What are the eight locks at Banavie, Invernesshire better known?
18. Where did Prince Charles Edward Stuart land in search of his father's throne in 1745?
19. Who built the first castle at Inverness in the 12th Century?
20. To which Loch did the osprey return in 1958?

THE MACALLAN GREAT SCOTS QUIZ

Quiz 5

1. On which river does Balmoral Castle lie?
2. Where was the opening sequence of Chariots of Fire shot?
3. Who scored Celtic's first goal when they won the European Cup in 1967?
4. Who opened the Forth Road Bridge?
5. Where in Edinburgh is the Central Library?
6. Which Scottish fishing port is famous for its smokies?
7. Which Robert Louis Stephenson novel was inspired by 'Deacon Brodie'?
8. Where is Captain Scott's Antarctic Research Vessel 'Discovery' now berthed?
9. Which member of The Skids went on to form Big Country?
10. Which Cathedral town was razed by fire on 26th August 1689?
11. Where is the official Loch Ness Monster Exhibition Centre?
12. What was the name of the TV show hosted by 'The Bay City Rollers'?
13. Who did Ken Buchanan defeat to win his World Boxing title?
14. Which Clan destroyed Strome Castle in 1602?
15. In European terms what did Glasgow become in 1990?
16. What was unique about Scotland's exit from the 1974 World Cup?
17. What is the city of Aberdeen known as?
18. Which two residents of Edinburgh regularly sold dead bodies to surgeons for medical research?
19. In golf where is the headquarters of the Royal and Ancient Club?
20. Where in Scotland does Captain Mark Philips run an Equestrian Centre?

Quiz 6

1. Who played Gregory in the film 'Gregory's Girl'?
2. Which town was the birthplace of Robbie Burns?
3. Which town has golf courses called Belleisle, Rozelle and Craigie?
4. Who opened Pitlochry's 'Theatre in the Hills' in 1981?
5. How deep is Loch Ness?
6. Which engineer built the Caledonian Canal?
7. Who defeated Bonnie Prince Charlie at Culloden in 1746?
8. In which year did the Forth Rail Bridge open?
9. In which year was Mary Queen of Scots born?
10. Who formally opened the Forth Rail Bridge?
11. What is the capital of the Island of Mull?
12. At which distance did Eric Liddell win an Olympic Gold Medal in 1924?
13. How many years did it take to build the Caledonian Canal?
14. What was the title of the Eurythmics first Top Ten Single?
15. Who did Aberdeen defeat to win the European Cup Winners Cup in 1983?
16. What was the title of Andy Stewart's Top Ten Single success of December 1989?
17. What is Scotland's most northerly ski resort?
18. Who designed the new golf course at Westerglen near Cumbernauld?
19. Who died on Loch Ness in 1952 during an attempt on the World Water Speed Record?
20. Who is the only Scotsman to captain England at Cricket?

THE MACALLAN GREAT SCOTS QUIZ

Quiz 7

1. Who is known as 'The Big Yin'?
2. Where was Mary Queen of Scots born?
3. What is the largest range of mountains on the Isle of Skye called?
4. Who was the compere of the 'White Heather Club'?
5. Which is the largest of the islands in the Outer Hebrides?
6. With which famous piece of music is the Island of Staffa associated?
7. Which two groups fought a battle at Glen Shiel in 1719?
8. What is unique about Ben Eigle, its Western Slopes and the area to Loch Clair?
9. What did Osgood McKenzie create at the head of Loch Ewe?
10. What was the title of Lulu's first Top Ten single?
11. What event took place on the evening of December 28th, 1879?
12. Who played Dr. Finlay in the TV series 'Dr. Finlay's Casebook'?
13. What was Annie Lennox before she became a Eurythmic?
14. Which Scottish City is situated at the confluence of the Dee and the Don?
15. Where was Shackleton's Ship the 'Terra Nova' built?
16. Which two Colleges merged in 1891 to form Aberdeen University?
17. In which year was Dundee created as a Royal Burgh?
18. Which Scottish female singer reached No. 43 in the charts in 1969 with 'Holy City'?
19. Who played Eric Liddell in the film 'Chariots of Fire'?
20. What was the title of the Bay City Rollers first Top 20 Hit?

Quiz 8

1. Which Scottish Castle has been the home of the Forbes and Forbes-Semphill family since it was built?
2. What takes place in Edinburgh during the last three weeks in August?
3. Which bird of prey returned to Scotland in 1958 after an absence of half a century?
4. Which Royal Burgh is known as the 'Capital of the Highlands'?
5. What is the name of the Southern Appendage of the Isle of Lewis?
6. Who had a Top Ten Hit in 1978 with 'Darlin'?
7. What is the highest peak in the Cuillin Range?
8. What is the name of the only surviving Gate of the Old Town Walls in Dundee?
9. Who was Scotland's team manager for the 1978 World Cup?
10. Where in Scotland is there a memorial to Flora McDonald?
11. On which TV show was Lena Zavaroni discovered?
12. Which association has its headquarters in Abertoff House, Inverness?
13. Who was the lead singer with The Rezillos?
14. At which sport other than athletics did Eric Liddell represent Scotland?
15. Who was the Chief of the McDonald Clan who died during the Glencoe Massacre in 1692?
16. Who had a No. 1 Hit in 1971 with 'Chirpy, Chirpy Cheep Cheep'?
17. By what is the mountain, Sgurr na Ciche, more commonly known?
18. Which Scottish team took part in the first ever European Cup Winners Cup Final in 1961?
19. What was the name of the French Ship which rescued Bonnie Prince Charlie in 1746?
20. To which Pretender was Jim Kerr of Simple Minds married?

THE MACALLAN GREAT SCOTS QUIZ

Quiz 9

1. What was B.A. Robertson's first Top Ten single?
2. What are the mountains, Aonoch Dubh, Gearr Aonoch and Beinn Fhada collectively known as?
3. Who did Glasgow Celtic defeat in the 1967 European Cup Final?
4. What is the County Town of Orkney mainland?
5. With which group did Midge Ure first achieve chart success?
6. Which game was almost certainly introduced to Scotland by the Flemings in the 15th Century?
7. What is the capital of The Shetlands?
8. Who was the youngest footballer ever to play for Scotland?
9. Where in Scotland is the famous museum of Childhood?
10. By what name is the mountain 'An Stac' better known?
11. What was the title of 'The Skids' only Top Ten single?
12. What is believed to be the second lowest Hollow in Europe?
13. Which footballer holds the Record for most Scottish International Caps?
14. In which Edinburgh Street will you find The Stock Exchange?
15. Where in Scotland will you find Loch Scridain?
16. Of which group is Marti Pellow the lead singer?
17. What does 'An Teallach' mean?
18. Who won the Mens 100m at the 1980 Moscow Olympics?
19. At which battle was Bonnie Prince Charlie finally defeated?
20. Who is the Patron Saint of Orkney?

Quiz 10

1. Which airport is situated at Sumburgh?
2. Which Middle East football team earned a creditable draw against Scotland in the 1978 World Cup Finals?
3. Who wrote Lulu's 1974 hit 'The Man Who Sold The World'?
4. Who laid out the new village of Ullapool in 1788?
5. Where is the prehistoric Ring of Brodgar?
6. Which Scottish athlete reached the final of the Womens 400m at the Moscow Olympics?
7. Which naturalist lived for a time on Tanera More and described his experiences in 'Island Year'?
8. Who played lead guitar with the 'Sensational Alex Harvey Band'?
9. What was the original capital of the Shetland Group?
10. In which country did Eric Liddell do most of his missionary work?
11. Which athlete won the 800m Gold Medal in the 1989 Europa Cup Final?
12. Which mountain in the Burgh of Dingwall is called Sugarloaf Mountain?
13. Who is the head of the Clan Campbell?
14. Of which Children's TV programme is John Leslie currently a presenter?
15. Who scored the winning goal for Nottingham Forest in the 1981 European Cup Final?
16. Where in Scotland will you find 'Seabury Chair'?
17. What were the first words spoken by Alexander Graham Bell on the telephone?
18. At which castle was the Marquis of Montrose captured prior to his execution in Edinburgh?
19. What is the total length of the River Spey?
20. What was Simple Minds first Top 20 Hit?

THE MACALLAN GREAT SCOTS QUIZ

Quiz 11

1. Where is the Spalding Golf Museum located in Dundee?
2. Who had a No. 1 Hit in October 1958 with 'Hoots Mon'?
3. Which monarch born in 1566 was the son of Mary Queen of Scots?
4. For whose Coronation was the Crown of the Scottish Regalia last used?
5. Who designed the Tay Rail Bridge which collapsed on December 28th, 1879?
6. By what other name was the City of Perth known until the 17th Century?
7. What was the name of Lulu's backing group?
8. Besides Alan Wells which other Scot was a member of the Great Britain 4 x 100m Relay team at the Moscow Olympics?
9. Into which Firth does Loch Lomond drain?
10. Who built the Perth Bridge of Nine Arches?
11. What is the Queen's Official Residence in Edinburgh?
12. Which group had a Top Ten Hit in 1973 with 'Broken Down Angel'?
13. Who won the 200m Breaststroke at the 1976 Montreal Olympics?
14. What are the remains of Iron Age Lake Dwellings in Scotland called?
15. Who holds the Record for Rowing the length of Loch Ness?
16. What town is regarded as the starting point of the road to the Isles?
17. Who composed the music 'Schottische' whilst on a visit to Gargurrock House?
18. Who was the name of the last of the male line of Scotland's native Royal Family?
19. What was remarkable about Brian Whittle's leg for Britain in the 4 x 400m Relay Final at the 1986 European Athletics Championships?
20. Which town is the Ferry terminal for the Island of Lewis?

Quiz 12

1. Who co-wrote the Band Aid single 'Do They Know It's Christmas' with Bob Geldof?
2. On which river does Dumfries stand?
3. Where in Edinburgh will you find 'John Knox's House'?
4. How many Grand Prix did Jackie Stewart win during his career?
5. Where was King Robert II crowned on 26th March 1371?
6. From which album was Rod Stewart's song 'Maggie May' taken?
7. What type of dog was Greyfriars Bobby?
8. What route runs from sea level at Fort William to sea level at Caernarvon via Ben Nevis, Scafell Pike and Snowdon?
9. Where did the last pitched battle on British soil take place?
10. Which Ultravox album reached No. 3 in the Charts and stayed in the Charts for 72 weeks?
11. Which fish reaches its most northerly point in Great Britain at Loch Lomond?
12. What is the name of Scotland's Highest village?
13. What is sprinter Allan Wells middle name?
14. Who was the lead singer with The Bay City Rollers?
15. What do the people of Gartocharn call 'The Dumpling'?
16. What is the name of Britain's largest Maternity Hospital?
17. What in Scotland is 2,573 miles long?
18. Which fish can only be found in Loch Lomond or Loch Eck?
19. Who wrote Rod Stewart's No. 1 Hit 'Sailing'?
20. Where does the River Endrick enter Loch Lomond?

THE MACALLAN GREAT SCOTS QUIZ

Quiz 13

1. Who was the lead singer with 'Stone The Crows'?
2. Which Scotsman invented the telephone?
3. Which extinct volcano near Edinburgh boasts the Salisbury Crags?
4. Which Hollywood actor played the part of Mr. Happer in the film 'Local Hero'?
5. For which Bond film did Sheena Easton sing the theme song?
6. Where are the ruins of Inchmahome priory?
7. What is the Gaelic word for church?
8. Who played Dr. Arnold in the BBC TV series 'Tom Brown's Schooldays'?
9. In which year did David II die?
10. What was Rod Stewart's first No. 1 solo single?
11. What is the official road number of the motorway linking Edinburgh with Glasgow?
12. What is the oldest regular regiment in the British Army?
13. Who wrote the theme music for the Tyne Tees TV series 'Supergran'?
14. Who wrote 'The Lady of the Lake'?
15. Where in Scotland will you find the grave of Robert the Bruce?
16. Which Loch is located in Abernethy Forest?
17. Which film starring Alec Guinness and John Mills was filmed mainly in a Scottish Castle?
18. Which American industrial millionaire was born in Dunfermline?
19. When was the last time Scotland failed to qualify for the World Cup Final stages?
20. Who had a No. 11 Hit in 1981 with 'Hold Me'?

Quiz 14

1. What was the name of Britain's 1969 Eurovision Song Contest entry sung by Lulu?
2. For what was Kenneth McAlpin who died in 860AD particularly famous?
3. Who succeeded Tony Jacklin as manager of the European Ryder Cup Team in 1989?
4. Which part did Iain Cuthbertson play in the TV series 'Budgie'?
5. Who occupied Falkland Palace in 1715 and proceeded to levy dues on the town?
6. What was Robinson Crusoe's real name?
7. Who married the daughter of King Robert II of Scotland in 1376?
8. Where is the oldest Seat of Learning in Scotland?
9. With which other group did The Sutherland Brothers team up with on their single 'Arms of Mary'?
10. From which castle did Mary Queen of Scots escape in 1567?
11. In which year was the Royal and Ancient Club founded at St. Andrews?
12. Which former Scottish football captain led Newcastle United to win the Inter-City Fairs Cup in 1969?
13. Which female singer appeared in the film 'Gregory's Girl'?
14. Who led a heroic defence against the English at Kildrummy Castle?
15. What is the official road number of the main road linking Glasgow and Carlisle?
16. Who wrote 'Peter Pan'?
17. What was the title of Billy Connolly's No. 1 Hit in 1975?
18. Which island in the Firth of Clyde lies due west of the town of Largs?
19. Which Scottish footballer was transferred twice to West ham during the 1980's from different Scottish clubs?
20. Which TV series starring Iain Cuthbertson was set in the area between England and Scotland?

THE MACALLAN GREAT SCOTS QUIZ

Quiz 15

1. Which monarch was murdered as he 'fled from the field of Sauchieburn'?
2. Who had a No. 2 Hit in 1970 with 'When I'm Dead and Gone'?
3. What was the War Cry of the Clan McFarlane?
4. Who wrote 'Sir Tristram' and 'The Lay of the Last Minstrel'?
5. In which Scottish town was 'Dr. Finlay's Casebook' set?
6. Where were the 1990 European Indoor Athletics Championships held?
7. Which famous museum is located in the Tayside village of Comrie?
8. Where are the tombs of Rob Roy McGregor and his family?
9. Who scored Scotland's third goal against Holland in the 1978 World Cup Finals?
10. What is the name of the oldest British warship still afloat?
11. Who had two No. 1 Hit albums entitled 'Rollin' and 'Once Upon A Star'?
12. In which range of mountains is Aviemore situated?
13. How old was Mary Queen of Scots when her father died?
14. Who accompanied the Explorer Speke in 1860-63 when searching for the source of the River Nile?
15. Where is the seat of the Earl of Moray?
16. Who had a No. 11 Hit in 1976 with 'Scotch On The Rocks'?
17. Who founded Kinloss Abbey
18. What is the Gaelic word meaning 'The Ridge of the Bridge'?
19. What castle stands at Strone Point on Loch Ness?
20. Whose home is Beaufort Castle?

Quiz 16

1. Who planned the Gardens At Crarae on Scotland's West Coast?
2. What is the Open Air Meseum at Auchindrain called?
3. Where was the 13th Century stronghold of the Macdougalls in Oban?
4. Of what is the small church in the village of Cormel on the A85 a miniature version?
5. Which Poet wrote "Child of Loud-Throated War? the mountainous stream" about Kilchurn Castle?
6. Who was the former Lead Singer with 'Marillion'?
7. Where was James Keir Hardie born?
8. The Emigrants from which village on Mull gave their name to a Canadian town?
9. Who had a hit in 1976 with 'Answer Me'?
10. To who, is the unique Scottish Monument in the village of Taynuilt dedicated?
11. What is the meaning of the Gaelic 'Ardnamurchan'?
12. Who built the first fortified structure at Fort William?
13. Who played Keyboards with Rod Stewart's band 'The Faces'?
14. Who captained Scotland in the 1974 World Cup Finals?
15. What is generally considered to be the jumping off point for the Isle of Skye?
16. What was first discovered at the village of Strontium in 1764?
17. What is the Administrative Centre for the Isle of Skye?
18. Which Scottish International scored both goals in the 1981 English F.A. Cup Final?
19. What is reputedly the most photographed Castle in Britain?
20. By what other name are the Hebrides known?

A PLACE CALLED MACALLAN

In the parish of Knockando, by the exuberant if
chilly waters of the Ringorm Burn that flows into the fabled
Spey, stands the ancient manor-house of
EASTER ELCHIES, for generations the nub of the activity
surrounding the production of The Macallan malt whisky.
*It is a matter of legend that whisky has been
produced here since the Middle Ages.*

Today, however, it is a matter of fact
that The Macallan is the best-selling malt at home on
Speyside. And every day its name and fame spread further
afield both at home and abroad: but although it has
come a long way from its misty origins,
it tastes not a whit less magical.

The Macallan. The Malt.

THE MACALLAN GREAT SCOTS QUIZ

Quiz 17

1. What type of event is held annually at Tobermory?
2. What is the alternative name for Pennycross?
3. What was known as the Cradle of Christianity in the Western Highlands?
4. Which Town lies at the Northern tip of Loch Long?
5. Which Glasgow Architect designed Hill House at Rhu near Helensburgh?
6. Which Loch off the A184 was a combined Operations Base in World War II?
7. What was the name of the last sea going Paddle Steamer in the world?
8. Who won the silver Medal in the 5000m at the 1970 Commonwealth Games in Edinburgh?
9. Where would you land on Mull if you took the Car Ferry from Oban?
10. Which Castle Ruins lie on the North Side of Salen Bay?
11. Of which Australian State was Lachlan McQuarrie Governor?
12. What joins the waters of Loch Gill with the Sound of Jura?
13. What is the Administrative Centre for Mid Argyll?
14. In what style is the Minard Castle built?
15. Whose Troops destroyed Bylen Castle on Kerrerra Island in 1645?
16. Who had a hit with 'Malt and Barley Blues" in 1971?
17. What is reputedly Scotland's Oldest Inn?
18. What is the Gaelic Word for Great Garden?
19. In which Robert Louis Stevenson novel was part of Appin featured?
20. In the famous 'Appin Murder' by what name was the victim, Colin Campbell, also known?

Quiz 18

1. Which Beatles song was a hit for 'Wet Wet Wet'?
2. What stretch of water separates Gourock from Dunoon?
3. Who built the House called 'Woodend' on the Isle of Bute?
4. Where is Highland Mary's Statue?
5. What was Lacklan McQuarrie also known as?
6. What does Tobermory mean in Gaelic?
7. In which year was James I of Scotland murdered?
8. Which English Monarch invaded Scotland in 1385?
9. Who was the second and last King of the House of Bruce?
10. What is the highest point on the island of Mull?
11. Who was the Founder of the House of Stuart?
12. For what type of musical event is the Central Hall of Glasgows Art Gallery sometimes used?
13. Which Glasgow Museum is located on Albert Drive?
14. Which Player missed a Penalty in Scotland's Opening Match of the 1978 World Cup Finals?
15. Why was Bonnie Prince Charlie unpopular with the City Father's of Glasgow?
16. How did Holy Loch derive its name?
17. Beside which Loch does the A815 from Sandback to Strachur run?
18. By what name is Ben Arthur also known?
19. Who brought Christianity to the Loch Lomond area in the 6th Century?
20. Who had a Top Thirty Hit in 1966 with 'A Man Without Love'?

THE MACALLAN GREAT SCOTS QUIZ

Quiz 19

1. In what year was the Battle of Killiecrankie fought?
2. Which Group had a hit with 'Real Gone Kid'?
3. Which Earl imprisoned James VI in 1582?
4. Who did Mary Queen of Scots marry in 1565?
5. At which Battle in 1542 were the Scots defeated by the English?
6. Which Monarch died at the Battle of Flodden Field?
7. Who had a hit with 'Temptation' in 1988?
8. Who murdered the 8th Earl of Douglas?
9. Which village lies at the Northern end of Gare Loch?
10. In which year was Aberdeen University founded?
11. Who married James III in 1496?
12. In which year were Orkney and Shetland annexed to Scotland?
13. What is the name of Glasgow's Oldest House?
14. Who defeated the English at Bell O'Brae in 1300?
15. What was the name of the first practical Passsenger Steamer in Europe?
16. Who is commemorated at Rhu near Helensburgh?
17. Where is the Tullock Library which was built in 1822?
18. Which Scottish Footballer was sent home in disgrace from the 1978 World Cup Finals?
19. What was Highland Mary's real name?
20. Which Scottish Town was the birthplace of John Logie Baird?

Quiz 20

1. Which Island in the Sound of Mull lies directly opposite Tobermory?
2. Where was the birthplace of David Livingstone?
3. Which family were Physicians to the Macleans of Duart for 300 years?
4. What was the name of the Naval Base on Mull during the Second World War?
5. Which place name in Scotland derived its name from a Settler named Jan De Groot?
6. To which Saint is the Well at Glossburn dedicated?
7. Which Pop Star made his home at Bolskine House near Foyers?
8. Which Food Manufacturing Company is based at Fochaber?
9. Where in Scotland is Sueno's Stone?
10. Which Company operates the Ferry between Hunters Quay, Dunoon and Gourock?
11. Who was known as the 'Wolf of Badenoch'?
12. From which country did the Gaels arrive in Scotland in the 5th Century?
13. What item of dress did Colonel Archibald Fraser help restore after it had been banned as an article of war?
14. Which 4 mile stretch of sand is overlooked by the grim ruin of Red Castle?
15. Who wrote 'The Thirty-Nine Steps'?
16. In which year was Bonnie Prince Charlie born?
17. Which International Goalkeeper did Glasgow Rangers sign from Norwich City?
18. Who was the last reigning Monarch of the House of Stuart?
19. Who scored Scotland's Goal in their 4-1 defeat by Brazil in the 1982 World Cup Finals?
20. Who defeated Charles II at the Battle of Worcester in 1650?

THE MACALLAN GREAT SCOTS QUIZ

Quiz 21

1. Who won the Gold Medal in the Women's 10,000m at the 1990 Commonwealth Games?
2. Which Publishing Company is responsible for Dennis The Menace?
3. What were discovered at the village of Strathfeffer in the 18th Century?
4. What was once described as 'a great Ocean Liner stranded among Golf Courses'?
5. What stretch of water lies between the South Coast of Scotland and the Cumbrian Coast?
6. Which Scottish Second Division Football Team play at Shieldfield Park?
7. Which Highland Novelist was born in Dunbeath?
8. Where do the family of actress Joanna Lumley originate from in Scotland?
9. Of which Pop Group is Ricky Ross a member?
10. Which Scottish Football Team lost to Gothenburg in the 1987 UEFA Cup Final?
11. On which river does Thurso lie?
12. Which race of people were called 'The Painted People'?
13. When were the Atomic Reactors at Dounreay built?
14. What stretch of water separates Orkney and the Scottish Mainland?
15. After whom was the village of Bettyhill named?
16. What is the Terminus of the West Highland Line?
17. What three natural phenomena can be seen from Duncansby?
18. Who currently owns the Castle of Mey?
19. What is the County Town of Caithness?
20. What is the most Northerly Point on the Scottish Mainland?

Quiz 22

1. Which Canadian Statesman was born in Dufftown in 1829?
2. Which Distillery was founded in 1824 by George Smith?
3. What is the highest village in the Grampian Region?
4. At which castle did Robbie Burns meet 'Bonny Lesley' whom he later immortalized in song?
5. Who captained Scotland during the 1982 World Cup Finals in Spain?
6. Which Monarch was called 'the Hammer of the Scots'?
7. Who was Scotland's first Post-Reformation Saint?
8. Who was the Highland Laddie of the song 'The Blue Bells of Scotland'?
9. Of which country did General Sir Hector McDonald become Governor?
10. Which Shakespearean Character was reputedly born in Dingwall?
11. Which main road skirts the southern shore of the Beauly Firth?
12. Which Highland Regiment raised in 1900 acted as a counter to the Boers in South Africa?
13. Who is buried at Erchless Motehill?
14. Which Earl's Home is Castle Lead?
15. Which Mountain in Scotland is also known as the Sugarloaf Mountain?
16. Which river passes through the Black Rock ravine?
17. In which town will you find the General Macdonald Memorial?
18. Who scored the winning goal in the 1978 European Cup Final?
19. Above which Firth will you find the Sidlow Hills?
20. Which is the Home Town of Scottish Athlete, Liz McColgan?

THE MACALLAN GREAT SCOTS QUIZ

Quiz 23

1. In which year did the first Jacobite Uprising take place?
2. Who was Scotland's goalkeeper in the 1978 World Cup Finals?
3. Which Scotsman in 1559 incited the Scots to attack Churches?
4. Who signed a Treaty of Perpetual Peace with England in 1501?
5. Which Scotsman invented a Steam Engine which could drive a rotating shaft in the 18th century?
6. Which German City is twinned with Aberdeen?
7. Who captained Scotland's Grand Slam Winning Rugby Union side of 1990?
8. In which year was the Battle of Flodden Field?
9. Where is Blairs College?
10. Where did Robert the Bruce sign the original Charter which gave the Lands of Drum to William de Irwin?
11. What is the county town of Banffshire?
12. What are the Bullers of Buchan?
13. Who was Britain's First Labour Prime Minister?
14. What was the name of the Borders Home of Sir Walter Scott?
15. Where in Scotland is there a Monument to the Fifth and last Duke or Gordon?
16. At which Village do the Gas Pipelines from the Brent and Ninian Fields reach the mainland?
17 Which Castle was the birthplace of Field Marshall James Keith?
18. Which Bram Stoker novel was allegedly inspired by Slains Castle?
19. Who founded the town of Dufftown in 1817?
20. Which Norwegian Composer 1843-1907 was of Scottish Ancestry?

Quiz 24

1. In which year was Glasgow University founded?
2. Which 230 million year old Fossils were found in Dumbarton Grove in 1887?
3. Which Scottish Inventor was responsible for the first Bicycle?
4. Why did Holyrood House fall into ruin in 1768?
5. Where were the Americas Cup Yachts, Sovereign and Sceptre built?
6. Where on Lock Eck was once the home of Sir Harry Lauder?
7. Who ordered ships to be dragged overland to Lock Lomond to hold onto his Scottish Lands?
8. What is the largest piece of fresh water in mainland Britain?
9. In which Scottish Village is there an effigy of St. Kessog?
10. Which Norwich City Player made his debut for Scotland against Argentina in March 1990?
11. What is the Stone Age Relic at Ardno called?
12. Where is reputedly the tallest tree in Scotland?
13. Which Scottish Singer released a single in the USA entitled 'Sugar Walls'?
14. Which two Glens link the sea locks of Loch Fyne and Loch Long?
15. Which Scottish Monarch was victorious at Loudoun Hill?
16. For which Rugby Union club does Damian Cronin play?
17. Who murdered the 'Red Comyn' in 1306?
18. In which year was the Declaration of Arbroath?
19. What was acknowledged at the Treaty of Northampton?
20. In which year did the Treaty of Union become law?

THE MACALLAN GREAT SCOTS QUIZ

Quiz 25

1. Where does the climax of the Highland Games Season take place?
2. By what name is the A939 better known?
3. In which Castle Garden will you find a Japanese water Garden?
4. In which Scottish Market Town is the Grampian Museum of Transport?
5. Who had a minor hit in 1988 with 'Chocolate girl'?
6. Whose home is Brechin Castle?
7. What type of fish is an Arbroath Smokie?
8. Which is the only non-Scottish football Team in the Scottish League?
9. Which is the oldest medieval Bridge in Scotland?
10. Where was the birthplace of Sir J. M. Barrie?
11. Of which Band was Eric Faulkner a Member?
12. What is the motto of Aberdeen?
13. Who founded a Monastery at Banchory in the 5th Century?
14. What event took place in Arboath Abbey in 1320?
15. In which city is Provost Skeene's House?
16. What happens in the village of Aboyne every August?
17. What was Footballer, Jim Baxter's Nickname?
18. Why did queen Victoria insist that the Deesside Railway ended at Ballater?
19. How many summits are there on the ridge of Lochnager?
20. Who played the part of Janet in the TV Series 'Dr. Finlay's Casebook'?

Quiz 26

1. For what type of Breakfast Food is Mrs. Keiller famous?
2. What is the meaning of the river named Allt Man Uamh?
3. Which two Clans fought a bloody battle at Tintean on the river Cassley in 1408?
4. Which town derives its name from the Norse 'Thing Vollr' meaning Council Place?
5. In which Battle of 1898 was General Sir Hector McDonald considered to have been a hero?
6. Where does the River Beauly become the River Glass?
7. Who was responsible for building Erchless Castle?
8. Which four Glens meet at the village of Cannich?
9. What according to tradition was first started at Carrimony in 1797?
10. What was the name of the Jet Engined Craft in which John Cobb died in 1952?
11. Who planned and built a new town at Fochabers in 1776?
12. Which Group had a No. 1 Album entitled 'Once Upon A Star'?
13. Who was Scotland's Manager for the 1990 World Cup finals?
14. What was the name of the first Scottish Missionary to India?
15. Which family have occupied Kilvarock Castle continuously since 1640?
16. In which town was Ramsey McDonald born?
17. What is the Twin Town of Macduff?
18. What kind of Students train at Blair's College?
19. What did the Gaels call their first Scottish Kingdom?
20. Which town was known as the 'Bath of Scotland' in the 18th Century?

THE MACALLAN GREAT SCOTS QUIZ

Quiz 27

1. Where was the 'Stone of Destiny' held prior to it being taken to Westminster Abbey?
2. Which Famous Engineer was called upon to complete the work on the Crinan Canal when it ran into problems?
3. How did the village of Furnace on Loch Fyne derive its name?
4. What is the name of the large uncompleted circular structure above Oban?
5. Where was James Stewart, James of the Glens, hanged?
6. Who had a No. 3 Hit Album entitled 'All For A Song'?
7. The name Loch Ailort derives its name from Norse. What does it mean?
8. Who are commemorated by Seven Beech Trees at Millhouse?
9. What was the 1843 Split in the Church of Scotland called?
10. After whom was Fort William named?
11. Where in Scotland will you find Arthur's Seat?
12. What was the original name of the Castle of Mey?
13. What product of Caithness can be found on the streets of cities throughout the world?
14. In which Town are the Scottish Publishers D. C. Thompson based?
15. Who was responsible for the clearances of 1812-19 in Strath Nawer?
16. Who wrote the 'Silver Darlings'?
17. Where is Jackie Stewart's Shooting School located?
18. What is the nickname of Dundee Utd. F. C.?
19. Where do 'The Broons" live?
20. In 1540 James V landed on Skye to try and resolve the feud between which two Clans?

Quiz 28

1. How many Scottish Kings look down upon Visitors to the Picture Gallery at Holyrood House?
2. Who painted 'Christ of St. John of the Cross' which is in Glasgow's Art Gallery?
3. In which year was Glasgow's Museum of Transport established?
4. In whose honour did Sir Harry Lauder erect an obelisk on a hill near his home?
5. What is displayed in the Clyde Room of the Museum of Transport in Glasgow?
6. Which player joined Celtic from West Ham and later transferred back to West Ham?
7. Where in Glasgow is there a comprehensive review of life in the city from 1715?
8. What is Barbara Dickson's Home Town?
9. When were the Botanic Gardens off Great Western Road in Glasgow founded?
10. Which annual gathering takes place in Dunoon every August?
11. On which road is there an Art Gallery including works by Goya, Murillo and El Greco in Glasgow?
12. How did the early McLeans of Duart summon up the devil when practising black magic?
13. Where did St. Columbus reputedly set foot on Mull en route to Iona?
14. Who lived at the House of Grulin above the shore of Loch Na Teal?
15. Where are the Poltalloch Stones?
16. Which Stone lies under the Coronation Chair at Westminster Abbey?
17. Which former Aberdeen and Celtic Player rejoined Newcastle United in 1989?
18. How many lochs are there on the Crinan Canal?
19. Who did James V marry in 1537?
20. Which Scottish Rugby International farms 1800 acres of the Duke of Roxburgh's Estate?

THE MACALLAN GREAT SCOTS QUIZ

Quiz 29

1. What links Tobermory with the Spanish Armada?
2. To what is the old Byre Museum on the Isle of Mull dedicated?
3. Whose body did David Livingstone help remove from the Gibbet and give a Christian burial?
4. For what purpose was the Cistercian Priory at Beauly used from 1470 to 1909?
5. Which Group had a No. 1 Album entitled 'Steeltown'?
6. Who wrote "In Highland Glens tis far too oft observed that man is chased away and game preserved"?
7. Where was Colonel James Grant, who accompanied Speke on his search for the source of the Nile, born?
8. Of which Military Architectural style is Fort George near Adersier an outstanding example?
9. Macduff and Banff lie on either side of which River estuary?
10. Which Loch is featured in Maurice Walsh's novel 'The Key Above The Door'?
11. In which city did General Sir hector McDonald die in 1903?
12. Who wrote the lines "Among the healthy hills and rugged woods the foaming foyers pours his messy floods"?
13. Which Scottish Chemist discovered Argon, Neon, Krypton and Xenon?
14. Which Team's Home Ground is Hampden Park?
15. How many Members of the European Parliament does Scotland have?
16. The Holly Trees in the Gardens of Gordon Castle are featured in which original song?
17. Which Anthem is played for Scotland at the Commonwealth Games?
18. Which Band had a Drummer called Michael 'Tich' Anderson?
19. Of which Canadian Bank did Lord Mount Stephen become President?
20. Who wrote the novel "Old Mortality"?

Quiz 30

1. Who was imprisoned by Elizabeth I in 1568 and executed in 1587?
2. At which Glasgow Club did Simple Minds make their debut appearance?
3. Who captured the Stone of Destiny in 1296 and took it to Westminster Abbey?
4. Who designed St. Columbus' Cathedral on the western side of the town of Oban?
5. Which Scottish Poet wrote 'The Bruce'?
6. Which family's 13th century Home is Castle Stalker?
7. Where was Scotland's first major Aluminium Plant built?
8. Who declared himself 'Guardian of Scotland' in 1297?
9. In which Group did Onnie McIntyre play Lead Guitar?
10. What is reputed to be the oldest inhabited Castle in Scotland?
11. Who wrote the novel 'Ring of Bright Water' and lived near the Kyle of Lochalsh?
12. Who was defeated and captured by the English at the Battle of Neville's Cross?
13. In which Sport did Jackie Stewart have considerable success prior to taking up Motor Racing?
14. In which year was Murdock, Duke of Albany executed?
15. Who was murdered at 'The Black Dinner'?
16. Which Group were originally 'Johnny and The Self Abusers'?
17. Who did James VI marry in 1589?
18. With which Group do you associate Roddy Frame?
19. Which Scottish Poet wrote 'Wallace'?
20. Which Scottish King was murdered at the Battle of Saucieburn?

THE MACALLAN GREAT SCOTS QUIZ

Quiz 31

1. Who founded a Monastery on the Island of Lismore in 562AD?
2. Which former Celtic player is now manager of Albion Rovers?
3. In which group would you find the Reid Brothers, William and JIm?
4. On which Firth does the town of Tain lie?
5. By what name is Maelbearha better known?
6. Which Scottish football team are nicknamed 'The Wasps'?
7. By what name is Derek William Dick better known?
8. On which Island will you find Loch Spelve?
9. Who ordered the rebuilding of the Monastery of Iona and was canonised in 1251?
10. Which Football Club play their Home Matches at Glebe Park?
11. What was the title of Gerry Rafferty's 4.5 Million Worldwide Seller of 1978?
12. Which Popular Scottish Resort is built on and around Kempock Point?
13. Who was the first Scottish King to issue his own autonomous coinage?
14. What is the connection between the grounds of Liverpool F.C. and Stirling Albion?
15. Which Group once played a 12 month Residency at The Top Storey Club in Edinburgh?
16. With which George Gershwin song did Bronski Beat have a hit in 1985?
17. Who was known as 'The Colossus of Roads'?
18. Where was the birthplace of the celebrated Preacher, Edward Irving?
19. What is the name of Edinburgh's Ice hockey Team?
20. Between which two Islands would you find the island of Gaunna?

Quiz 32

1. Which Saint who died of the Plague in 548 AD established Christian Churches at Iona, Mull and Tiree?
2. Which Football Club play their Home Matches at Broomfield Park?
3. Which is the Home Town of Gallagher & Lyle?
4. Which Hebridean Island lies between North and South Uist?
5. Who was the King of the Scots of Dalriada in 843 Ad?
6. Up to the end of the 1989-90 Season how many times had Rangers won the Scottish League?
7. With which Group was Dean Ford the Lead Vocalist?
8. On which Loch do the forests of Inverlever & Eredine stand?
9. Why did Princess Margaret of England take refuge in Scotland in 1066?
10. Which Club knocked Rangers out of the Scottish Cup in 1967?
11. Which Folk-Based Group featured the talents of Billy Connolly, Gerry Rafferty and Tom Harvey?
12. Which Ferry Port stands at the head of Loch Ryan?
13. To whom was the Island of Iona ceded in 1098?
14. Which Scottish Football Club are nicknamed 'The Bully Wee'?
15. Where will you find scotland's only Safari Park?
16. Who sang he original version of The Communards Hit, 'Don't Leave me This Way'?
17. Who built the Bridge over the River Nith at Auldgirth?
18. Which Scottish League football Team were managed in the early 1970's by Bob Shankly?
19. On which Island will you find Loch Sresort?
20. What is the name of Edinbugh's Main Railway Station?

THE MACALLAN GREAT SCOTS QUIZ

Quiz 33

1. Who established a Monastery near Whithorn on the Solway known as Candida Casa?
2. Who was Aberdeen's Record signing in January 1988?
3. What was Sheena Easton's debut record release?
4. On what stretch of water does the Town of Invergordon lie?
5. At which Battle did the Picts defeat King Ecgfrith in 685AD?
6. What is the name of the now traditional 'Curtain Raiser' to the Scottish League Season?
7. Which American Actor starred with Lulu in the film 'To Sir With Love'?
8. On which Sea Loch does the town of Inverary stand?
9. Who was known to his contemporaries as Ceann Mor or Bighead?
10. From which club did Liverpool sign Steve Nicol in 1981?
11. Which Musician formed Stealers Wheel in 1972?
12. Why was Robert Louis Stevenson stoned at Ballantrae in 1878?
13. Who ruled Scotland after the death of Malcolm III?
14. Which Player has made the most appearances for Celtic?
15. What is the Home of the Argyll and Southern Highlanders?
16. What was the title of Lloyd Cole and the Commotions first album?
17. Which Band had a Guitarist called Stuart 'Woody Wood'?
18. How long did Macbeth reign in Scotland?
19. Which Scottish Philosopher wrote 'Treatise of Human Nature'?
20. On which river does Glasgow stand?

DOWN
1 The Malt (3-8).

THE MACALLAN GREAT SCOTS QUIZ

Quiz 34

1. In which year did Bill Shankly take over as Manager of Liverpool?
2. Who had a No 5 Hit Album entitled 'Easy Pieces'?
3. Where did James II defeat the Douglases?
4. Who is the Patron Saint of Scotland?
5. In which film did the Bronski Beat Song 'Hit That Perfect Beat' feature?
6. Which Company manufacture Green Hunter Field Boots?
7. What is monitored at Eskdalemuir Observatory?
8. When was the present Castle at Balmoral built?
9. Which Master of Scots Fiddle Music is commemorated by a Memorial Tablet in Banchory High Street?
10. Over which Scottish Town did Pan Am Flight 103 crash in December 1988?
11. Apart from Jimi Somerville who were the other members of Bronski Beat?
12. Who was known as The Wolf of Badenoch?
13. What did the Gaels call their first Scottish Kingdom?
14. After Balmoral which is the most popular Castle with visitors in Scotland?
15. Which Scottish Band made their first appearance at the Lincoln Festival?
16. Which Scottish football Club play at Rugby Park?
17. Which F.I.F.A. World Cup was held in Scotland in 1989?
18. Which famous rock lies 3 miles off the Scottish Coast at North Berwick?
19. By what is Marie McDonald Lawrie better known?
20. Into which stretch of water does the River Nith flow?

Quiz 35

1. Which Scotsman is the Manager of Arsenal?
2. Why was Alexander Stuart, Earl of Buchan excommunicated?
3. Who had a hit with 'Smalltown Boy' in 1984?
4. Which Scottish Writer ended the last 5 years of his life as Governor-General of Canada?
5. What was the title of Lloyd Cole's only Top 20 Hit?
6. Which Monarch was defeated at Flodden in 1513?
7. Where in Scotland is the Pictish Sculptured Stone Cross known as the Formaston Stone?
8. Which Group featured the Sax Players Roger Ball and Malcolm 'Molly' Duncan?
9. Which Scottish Football Club are Nicknamed 'The Jags'?
10. Which famous singing brother did Lulu marry in 1969?
11. Which Scotsman co-presents 'The Saint & Greavsie Show'?
12. On which Island will you find Loch Bracadale?
13. Which Political Party won th 1967 Hamilton By-Election?
14. Who wrote 'A Race of Men, the wind of whose name has swept the ultimate seas'?
15. Who was the first Leader of the Free Church of Scotland?
16. Who was the first Secretary of the Scottish Miners Association?
17. In which year was the Scottish Labour Party founded?
18. From which Club did Celtic buy Andy Walker?
19. Who was Manager of Rangers prior to Graeme Souness?
20. What was the name of the Wall built by the Romans from the Clyde to the Forth in 141AD?

THE MACALLAN GREAT SCOTS QUIZ

Quiz 36

1. Which Group's First Album was entitled 'The Crossing'?
2. Near which city was the Battle of Pinkie fought in 1547?
3. Who played Lead Guitar with the Average White Band?
4. From what material are the majority of buildings in Aberdeen built?
5. Which Scottish Castle was the scene of Duncan's Murder?
6. Which Group started life as the Absorbic Ones?
7. What is the name of the Atomic Research Station near Thurso?
8. Who replaced Alan Longmuir in the Bay City Rollers?
9. Who runs the steam trains between Aviemore and Boat of Garten?
10. Apart from Fort William and Fort George what other example of Hanoverian Military Architecture can be found in the Highlands?
11. Whose first single was entitled 'Perfect Skin'?
12. Which famous Golf Course lies 10 miles west of Kilmarnock?
13. Which Scottish Actor starred in the BBC2 Series 'Mistero Buffo' in 1990?
14. What did Alexander Fleming discover in 1929?
15. In which Town was Archbishop of Canterbury Robert Runcie born?
16. Which Scottish Entertainer stars with Liam Neeson in the film 'The Big Man'?
17. Which two players finished second in the 1990 British Open Golf Championship?
18. Which Scottish Group played two sell-out Concerts at Wembley Arena on 13th and 14th December 1984?
19. What is Britain's only Triangular Castle?
20. What was the Bay City Roller's only U.S. No 1 Single?

Quiz 37

1. What is the Home Town of Stuart Adamson of Big Country?
2. How often does the town of Brigadoon reputedly appear?
3. Where did the German Fleet scuttle its ships at the end of the First World War?
4. Who is the Lead Singer with the Communards?
5. Which TV Service began broadcasting on 30th September 1961?
6. Who replaced Robbi McIntosh in the Average White Band?
7. Where was the first British Open Golf Championship held in 1860?
8. In which city was the Encyclopaedia Britannica first published in 1768?
9. Who was the manager with The Bay City Rollers?
10. What is the Home Town of Golfer Sam Torrance?
11. Which Donna Summer song did Bronski Beat take to No 3 in the UK Charts?
12. What is Scotlands most southerly Distillery?
13. Which member of Dad's Army came from Dumfries?
14. What did Robbie Burns describe as a 'Wee Sleekit cowrin timorous Beastie'?
15. When were the Special Licences at the Blacksmiths Shop at Gretna Green made illegal?
16. Who wrote the lines 'Marriage is like life in this, that it is a field of battle and not a bed of roses'?
17. What is the title of the Head of the Clan Campbell?
18. Which Group played their first live Gig at a Glasgow Pub called 'The Countdown'?
19. Who directed the film 'Gregory's Girl'?
20. Which Group had a Vocalist called Hamish Stuart?

THE MACALLAN GREAT SCOTS QUIZ

Quiz 38

1. Which Celtic Mythological Hero by tradition used to tether his dog in the town of Oban?
2. What were Henry VIII's Invasions of Scotland called in 1544 & 1545?
3. What is the Time Difference between Perth Scotland and Perth, Australia?
4. In which year were the Court of Justices, later called 'The Session' founded?
5. Which Group had a No 9 Hit with 'Party Fears Two'?
6. What is the French Word for Scotland?
7. Where is the Home of the Athlete, Steve Ovett?
8. Where is Britain's only Buddhist Temple?
9. Which two Families took part in a bitter feud lasting 100 years which ended with the destruction of Strome Castle?
10. When were the supporters of David II defeated by Edward II in 1333?
11. Who had a No 2 L.P. entitled 'Mainstream' in the UK Charts?
12. Which Group had a Top 20 Hit with the song, 'There's More To Love'?
13. Where was the centre of the 'Gold Fever' of 1867-69 in the far north of Scotland?
14. What are the projectiles used in Curling called?
15. At which University did Britain's first Professor of Parapsychology take up his post?
16. Which two English Soccer Internationals won their 70th Caps against Scotland in th same match?
17. Which incident is thought to have inspired the poisoning scene in 'Macbeth'?
18. Which Scottish Football Team is nicknamed 'The Dee'?
19. Who besieged Dunbeath Castle in 1650 and captured it after 3 days?
20. Which Group had a UK Chart Hit in 1986 entitled 'Look Away'?

Quiz 39

1. Who said 'Football is not a matter of life and death, it's more important than that'?
2. In which Group did the Longmuir Brothers play?
3. Which Coin was known as a Bawbee in Scotland?
4. What was Britain's biggest selling single prior to 'Do They Know It's Christmas'?
5. Which Island lies opposite the Town of Oban in Oban Bay?
6. Who has lived continuously in Dunvegan Castle for the past 700 years?
7. Which part of the East Coast of Canada derives its name from Scotland?
8. What is the name of Jimmy Logan's singing Sister?
9. Which Novel was inspired by the murder of John Campbell of Glenure in 1752?
10. Where in Scotland was the Old Prison known as The Tollbooth?
11. Where do Scotland play their Home Rugby Union Internationals?
12. Which Port on Hong Kong Island is named after a Scottish City?
13. Who was responsible for the 'Clearances' of 1812-1819 in Strath Naver?
14. Where is the main Ferry Port for the Orkneys and The Faroes?
15. What are Freckles called in Scotland?
16. Of which Soccer Trophy were Scotland the first winners in 1985?
17. By what name is Locomotive 4472 better known?
18. For what purpose were Shetland Ponies used in the 19th Century?
19. Which Group's First Album was entitled 'Age of Consent'?
20. What is unique about Loch Morar?

THE MACALLAN GREAT SCOTS QUIZ

Quiz 40

1. Which two teams had just played at Ibrox when 66 Spectators were killed in 1971?
2. The Inhabitants of which Island were once called 'Scottis'?
3. Where was the Racing Driver, Jim Clark, killed?
4. How did Madeleine Smith come to public attention in Glasgow in 1857?
5. What does the F.P. stand for in Heriots F.P.?
6. Which Australian Club won the Melrose Sevens in 1990?
7. What is Scotland's most famous Athletics Stadium?
8. Who was actually 'Kidnapped' in the book of the same name?
9. Which former Manager of Wolverhampton Wanderers once said, 'I opened the Trophy cabinet and two Japanese Prisoners of War came out'?
10. What kind of Eggs are wrapped in Sausage Meat?
11. Which Queen is said to haunt Borthwick Castle?
12. What are Thistle, Ninian, Piper and Beryl?
13. What was the name of Mary Queen of Scots' famous Horse?
14. What do Scots call 'Champit Tatties'?
15. What would you be holding if you were given a 'Bairn' in Scotland?
16. In which City is 'The Prime of Miss Jean Brodie' set?
17. Which Fish is also called a 'Glasgow Magistrate'?
18. Which song gave the Pipes and Drums of the Royal Scots Guards a No 1 Hit?
19. How many teams compete in the Scottish Premier Football Division?
20. Which Group's Debut L.P. was called 'High Land, hard Rain?

SCIENTIST Discovers Reason for Universe
(Continued from page 2)

the parabolic cylinder function of the Confluent hypergeometric, gives Hermitian Polynomial

$$H_n\left(\frac{z}{\sqrt{2}}\right) \equiv 2^{n/2} e^{z^2/4} D_n(z) = 2^n \psi\left(-\frac{n}{2}, \frac{1}{2}; \frac{z^2}{2}\right);$$

expansion of the orthogonal function, with fourier coefficients given as $|f\rangle$; the explicit expression gives

$$\lim_{k \to \infty} \left\{ \langle f | - \sum_{i=1}^{k} \langle e_i | f^{-i} \rangle \right] \left[|f\rangle - \sum_{j=1}^{k} f^{(j)} |e_j\rangle \right] \right\} = \lim_{k \to \infty} \left\{ \langle f | f \rangle - \sum_{i=1}^{k} |f^{-i}|^2 \right\}$$

the Bessel & Error functions are written

$$\frac{d^2 u}{dz^2} + \frac{1}{z}\frac{du}{dz} + \left(1 + \frac{v^2}{z^2}\right) u = 0 \quad ; \quad Erf(z) = \int^z e^{-t^2} dt = z \Phi\left(\frac{1}{2}, \frac{3}{2}; -z^2\right)$$

$$W'_{r \cdots} = \frac{2}{5}(x^{-i}) = (D^{-1})^{\rho}_{k} \cdots (D^{-1})^{q}_{r} D^{m}_{s} \cdots 0 D^{k}_{s} w^{k \cdots c}_{m \cdots n} (D_j x^{-j})$$

$$\sum_{i=1}^{\infty} |a^{-i} + b^2|^2 = \sum_{i=1}^{\infty} |a^{-i}|^2 + \sum_{i=1}^{\infty} |b^{-i}|^2 + 2Re\left\{\sum_{i=1}^{\infty} b^{-i} a^{-i}\right\}; \text{ tensor rank } N, \& \text{ Hilbert Space.}$$

the Hermitian orthogonal functions $\psi_n(x) = N_n e^{-\xi^2/2} H_n(\xi)$; applies

$$\int \psi_n^2(x) dx = 1 \quad ; \quad N_n = \left\{\left(\frac{\alpha}{\pi}\right)^{1/2} \frac{1}{2^n n!}\right\}^{1/2} \quad ; \quad \int \psi_m(x) \psi_m(x) dx = 0 \quad ; \quad \text{for}$$

$$S(\xi, s) = \sum \frac{H_n(\xi)}{n!} s^n = e^{\xi^2 - (s-\xi)^2} \quad ; \quad T(\xi, t) = \sum \frac{(\xi)}{m!} H_m t_m = e^{\xi^2 - (t-\xi)^2}$$

we may now extend this analysis to develop the 'neoteric universal equation'.

(Continued on page 63)

THE MACALLAN GREAT SCOTS QUIZ

Quiz 41

1. What type of Monster was the 'Glaistig'?
2. Which City is famous for 'Jute Jam & Journalism'?
3. Which Scottish Football Club are known as the 'Academicals'?
4. On which river is Stirling Situated?
5. What is Leadhill famous for?
6. Which Scottish Football International played for Bayern Munich in the 1989-1990 Season?
7. Who 'lost her head' in 1587?
8. In which Sport did Paul Masson captain Scotland?
9. Of whom was Lord Darnley the second husband?
10. Who in the world of Football is known as 'The Doc'?
11. Who recorded the song 'Just Like Kenny'?
12. Which river provides the Border between Scotland and England?
13. To which point does The Royal mile lead from Edinburgh Castle?
14. Why did it take James VI 3 days to learn he had become King of England?
15. Besides Motor Racing with which other sport is Jackie Stewart asociated?
16. How did Average White Band Drummer, Robbie McIntosh die?
17. Which Group features Roddy Frame on Vocals and Guitar?
18. Who had the original hit with the Bay City Rollers Hit 'Bye Bye Baby'?
19. What is the connection between the Earl of Carrick and the Duke of Rothesay?
20. What Title is given to the Chief Herald in Scotland?

Quiz 42

1. Which General is said to haunt Blackness Castle and also founded the Scots Greys?
2. Which BBC Sports Reporter was a former Scottish International Goalkeeper?
3. On which River was the QE2 built?
4. How many people were murdered by Burke & Hare?
5. Where do Orcadians come from?
6. How many Divisions comprise The Scottish Football League?
7. Who was sentenced to have his nose cut off for making fun of Scotsmen?
8. Which Scottish Town has the same name as a Candle Component?
9. What is the date of 'Burns Night'?
10. What is a 'Cullen Skink'?
11. What is 'Ogham'?
12. In which Sport can you win the Strathcona Cup?
13. What is the most visited building in Scotland?
14. Which sport features in the film 'Gregory's Girl'?
15. Which Politician was named 'head of the Year' in 1984?
16. Which Castle is said to be haunted by Mary Queen of Scots?
17. Where in Scotland will you find The Wallace Monument?
18. Which Scottish Town has most often won the 'Britain in Bloom' Award?
19. What is 'Barlinnie'?
20. What is a 'Bubblyjock' in Scotland?

THE MACALLAN GREAT SCOTS QUIZ

Quiz 43

1. Where is Britain's Oldest Working Post Office?
2. What was the Average White Band's only US No 1 Hit?
3. Who cooked the 'Eye of Newt and Toe of Frog. Wool of Bat and Tongue of Dog'?
4. Which is the Home Town of the Group 'The Associates'?
5. What was the Mascot for the 1986 Commonwealth Games?
6. What was the Bay City Rollers last Chart Success in the U.K.?
7. Who defeated the supporters of David II at the Battle of Daplin Moor?
8. Of which Scottish Athletic Club is Steve Ovett a Member?
9. Where did Robbie Burns spend the last seven years of his life?
10. Which former 'Professional' has a Holiday Home near Carsluith?
11. Which Pop Group had a Guitar and Keyboard Player called Jim McIven?
12. Which girlfriend of film Director, Michael Winner, played an Oceanographer in the film 'Local hero'?
13. Which Scottish Stone was used in the construction of the Sydney Harbour Bridge?
14. What is unique about the Star hotel, Moffat?
15. Of which Group were Billy McKenzie and Alan Rankine members?
16. For what material is the Isle of Harris renowned?
17. Which Song begins 'Maxwelton's braes are bonnie'?
18. How deep is Loch Ness?
19. What type of tree was named after David Douglas?
20. Who was responsible for forming a model industrial community in Scotland in the early 19th Century?

Quiz 44

1. Who wrote 'The best laid plans of mice and men ...gang aft agley'?
2. Which Stone did Edward I steel from Scotland?
3. Which Group had a Bass Player named Tony Butler?
4. Which former member of Bros hails from Kirkcaldy?
5. What is the title of Fairground Attraction's No 1 Hit Single?
6. In which year did the English Parliament pass The Act of Settlement in favour of Hanoverian Succession?
7. In which year was Patrick Stuart, the Earl of Orkney executed?
8. Which Flat Racing Jockey was a former Team Captain on 'A Question of Sport'?
9. In which year did James IV marry Margaret Tudor?
10. With which former Gloria Gaynor song did the Communards have a No 4 Hit in 1987?
11. Where and when was Jack Bruce of the Group 'Cream' born?
12. Which Monarch was accidentally killed at the siege of Roxburgh?
13. Which Poet wrote the poem which has come to be known as 'The Thistle and the Rose'?
14. Which London Club signed Charlie Nicholas from Celtic?
15. With which Group did Big Country's, Tony Butler, previously play Bass Guitar?
16. For whom was Kinmount House near Dumfries built?
17. Who is the only manufacturer of golf Balls in Scotland?
18. From which Club did Rangers sign Trevor Steven and Gary Stevens?
19. Where was Author J.M.Barrie? educated?
20. Which Town is known as the 'Queen of the South'?

PICTURE QUIZ

1. Name this bridge?

2. Who is this lady?

3. What is his nick name?

4.. Name this castle?

5. Whose monument is this?

6. What was his former profession?

(a) Name the tartan?

7. Who is he and why was he unique?

8. Name the actor and the film?

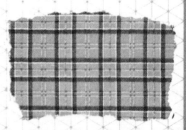

(b) Name the tartan?

THE MACALLAN GREAT SCOTS QUIZ

Quiz 45

1. Who is the Lord of the Isles?
2. Who wrote the words to 'Auld Lang Syne'?
3. Whose former Official Residence was Spynie Castle, North of Elgin?
4. Who had a Research Station at Fraserburgh from which Radio Signals were sent to Receiving Stations in England?
5. Which Group had a No 14 L.P. entitled 'Shine'?
6. How did the Bay City Rollers get their name?
7. In which year did Scottish TV begin broadcasting?
8. Which Keyboard Player formed The Communards with Jimi Somerville?
9. Who won the 100th Scottish Cup Final in 1985?
10. Which red & green substance found in the Portsoy District was used in the finishing of the Palace of Versailles?
11. What kind of Students train at Blairs College?
12. Which Company operate a factory near Dumfries which produces Melinex Polyester Film?
13. What is the name of the Drummer with 'Big Country'?
14. Which Group consists of Elizabeth Frazer, Robin Guthrie and Simon Raymonde?
15. Who was known as the M.P. in the Cloth Cap?
16. With which Group does Eddie Reader sing?
17. At which venue did Nick Faldo win his first British Open title?
18. Who was the first Catholic Footballer to play for Glasgow Rangers?
19. Which Amateur Golfer sank the Winning Putt in the 1989 British Walker Cup Victory in America?
20. From which Football Club did Rangers sign Mark Walters?

Quiz 46

1. On which BBC Tv show did the Group Marillion make their TV debut?
2. What did the J.M. stand for in J. M. Barrie's name?
3. What in Scotland is a Shieling?
4. What is the name of the Ugly Sister in 'The Broons'?
5. Who is the Countess of Inverness?
6. In which Nature Reserve will you find Stac Pollaidh, Cul Nor and Cul Beag?
7. Which Scottish Football Club previously played at Meadows, Powderhall and Mayfield?
8. At the foot of which mountain are the ruins of Wrearbo Castle?
9. Which town stands on the confluence of the Urr Water and the Kirkgunzeon Lane?
10. Which hills separate England from Scotland?
11. From which club did Celtic sign Mick McArthy?
12. Who was the first U.K. girl singer to appear behind the Iron Curtain?
13. Which Scottish Protestant was responsible for the book 'The First Book of Discipline'?
14. What nationality were the bodysnatchers Burke and Hare?
15. Which hills were formerly one hill until Michael Scott, the Border Wizard, split them with the help of the devil?
16. Which Scottish Football Club are nicknamed 'The Warriors'?
17. In which J.M. Barrie novel would you find 'The Lost Boys'?
18. Which town is the capital of the Galloway Region?
18. On which river is Gatehouse of Fleet situated?
20. Which pop group began life as The Vortex Motion?

PICTURE QUIZ

9. Name the bridge?

10. Name this lead singer?

11. Name the castle?

12. What is pictured here?

13. Name the politician?

14. Name this town?

(c) Name the tartan?

(d) Name the tartan?

PICTURE QUIZ

15. Name the team?

16. Name the group (minus lead singer)?

17. Name the castle?

18. Name this building?

19. Who is this?

20. Name this singer?

21. Who is this lady?

24. Who is this lady and who did she marry?

(e) Name the tartan?

23. Name the M.P. and his shadow cabinet position?

22. Who is he and what award did he win in 1989?

THE MACALLAN GREAT SCOTS QUIZ

Quiz 47

1. Which famous Scotsman had a roadbuilding material named after him?
2. What is a Barrister called in Scotland?
3. What item of attire did Marmalade wear on Top of the Pops when 'Ob la Di Ob La Da' was No. 1?
4. Who scored the winning goal in the 1965 English F.A. Cup Final?
5. What was the purpose of 'Operation Deep Scan' in 1987?
6. What is the name of the bespectacled bookworm in 'The Broons'?
7. What are the 'Sutors of Cromarty'?
8. What happened to Patrick Hamilton in 1528 when he refused to recant?
9. Who lost his voice in September 1985 which caused the cancellation of a 23 date tour?
10. Which English Football Club was managed by Jock Stein in 1978?
11. By what name is Iain Tennant also known?
12. What was the name of the world's first prototype Fast Breeder Reactor?
13. What in Scotland is exactly 4408 feet high?
14. Who in 1174 renounced his Feudal superiority over Scotland in return for 10,000 Marks?
15. What was the home of Thomas Carlyle from 1828 to 1834?
16. What is Usquebaugh?
17. What is the name of Britain's only private army?
18. By what other name was William Duke of Cumberland known in Scotland?
19. Where did Egypt defeat Scotland 3–1 in a friendly International in May 1990?
20. Which great yachting event will Scotland enter for the first time in 1992?

Quiz 48

1. What is the Scottish equivalent of a District Attorney?
2. Who captained Sunderland when they won the 1973 English F.A. Cup Final?
3. Where was the Republic of Ireland Soccer International, Ray Houghton, born?
4. Who is the present Earl of Inverness?
5. What and where is Mons Meg?
6. Who would have used 'Squinches' or 'Squints' in Scottish Churches?
7. Which Scottish painting job requires 7000 gallons of paint?
8. Which 1980's film starring Sean Connery was about an immortal Clansman named McCloud?
9. Where would you find Polliwillime Bay?
10. Who defeated Ecfrith of Northumbria at the battle of Nechtansmere in 685AD?
11. How did Fish of Marillion derive his name?
12. Who was Celtic's goalkeeper when they won the European Cup in 1967?
13. What are the 'Twelve Apostles' near Dumfries?
14. Where did Robbie Burns write his poems 'Tam O Shanter' and 'Ye Banks and Braes'?
15. Who was the last of the Covenanting martyrs executed at Edinburgh in 1688?
16. Who built the bridge over the River Nith at Auldgirth?
17. For what purpose was a 'Doocot' used?
18. In which year was Strathclyde annexed to Scotland?
19. Which Scottish club are nicknamed 'The Buddies'?
20. After his defeat at Culloden what price was put on the head of Bonnie Prince Charlie?

THE MACALLAN GREAT SCOTS QUIZ

Quiz 49

1. Which famous sailing ship built in 1870 has the same name as a brand of Whisky?
2. From which club did Celtic sign Mark McGhee?
3. What was a Reiver?
4. Who was the Master of Greyfriars Bobby?
5. Who was the Assistant Manager of Celtic during the 1989-1990 season?
6. What is the Cross of St. Andrew?
7. Who wrote the McGuiness Flint single 'When I'm Dead And Gone'?
8. What is the name of the part of Wester Ross between Loch Broom and the Sutherland Border?
9. Between which two points did the World's First Train Ferry run in 1849?
10. Where are the Headquarters of the Scottish Office in London?
11. What is the oldest form of rock found in Britain?
12. Which two Scottish Islands are separated by the Sound of Harris?
13. By what name was Donald Dubh, the son of Angus Og also known?
14. What was the name of James IV's Warship which he believed to be the mightiest in Europe?
15. On which Waterway does the town of Dingwall lie?
16. On which river does the town of Brechin lie?
17. Which Scottish Football Club paid £14,000 to buy Harry Hood from Sunderland in 1966?
18. What was the title of the last film in which Sean Connery played James Bond?
19. Which pop group's fan club is called 'The Web'?
20. What is the name of the Queen's Bodyguard in Scotland?

Quiz 50

1. What is Scotland's heaviest ever defeat in the World Cup Finals?
2. Who was born in the 'Arched House' in 1795?
3. Where was the Cutty Sark built?
4. What was worth 53s 4d in the reign of James IV?
5. Which Scottish actor played the Old Lighthouse keeper in Fraggle Rock?
6. From which club did Rangers sign Richard Gough?
7. On which seaway will you find the town of Invergordon?
8. What in Scotland is a Toft?
9. What were the Churchill Barriers used to block?
10. In which European City did Bonnie Prince Charlie die?
11. Who was Celtic's leading scorer in the 1988-89 season?
12. Which Scottish Football Club play at Kilbowie Park?
13. How many yards were there in a Scottish mile?
14. Which Scottish Football Club are nicknamed 'The Sons'?
15. For what did Andrew Millar and Walter Chapman receive a Royal Patent in 1507?
16. Who scored Scotland's opening goal in the 1974 World Cup Finals?
17. What is a Philibeg?
18. What did Alan Pinkerton establish in America in the 19th Century?
19. What does 'Clann' mean in Gaelic?
20. Of which Clan was Buachaille nan Eileann the Gaelic title?

PICTURE QUIZ

25. Name this lady?

26. Which racecourse?

27. Name this 'palace'?

28. La Terrasse, Le Cafe D'Harcourt was painted by whom?

29. Where and what is this annual event?

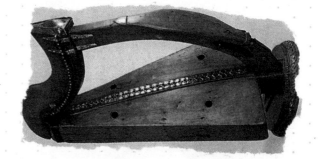

30. What is this famous instrument called?

PICTURE QUIZ

31. Where is this building situated?

32. In which town is this building?

33. Where does he live?

34. What part did he play in Dad's Army?

38. Name this course?

39. Name this man?

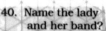

40. Name the lady and her band?

37. Who is this clergyman?

36. Who is this golfer?

35. Name this man?

THE MACALLAN GREAT SCOTS QUIZ

Quiz 51

1. Which Scottish League Football Club are nicknamed 'The Doonhammers'?
2. Where on Scotland's East Coast is Codonas Amusement park?
3. Of which river estuary does the Sands of Forvie Bird Reserve form part?
4. Which famous coat company has its headquarters on the River Don, 3 miles from Aberdeen?
5. Who did Sheena Easton duet with on 'We've Got Tonight' in 1983?
6. With which group does Tina Weymouth play bass guitar?
7. Which Scottish king died at Cardross in 1329?
8. Where is the Island of Inchcolm?
9. What is a Bridie?
10. Who had a hit album entitled 'Year of the Cat'?
11. Which First Class County Cricket side did Scotland defeat in the 1990 Benson and Hedges Cup?
12. What is the 'Devil's Beef Tub'?
13. What is the link between St. Johnstone and Southampton Football Clubs?
14. For which English Football Club did Ally McCoist play?
15. Whose heart is buried at Melrose Abbey?
16. What is a Yakmac?
17. Where in Scotland is the Silver Staircase?
18. Which animal became extinct in Scotland in 1743?
19. Which Dutch Football team defeated Celtic in the 1969 European Cup Final?
20. Which great Philanthropist once lived at Cawdor Castle?

Quiz 52

1. Which group reached No. 14 in the U.K. Charts with 'Once In A Lifetime'?
2. What was bestowed on Edward Bruce by the people of Ireland in 1316?
3. Which Scottish goalkeeper was dropped by Manchester United for the replayed 1990 English F.A. Cup Final?
4. Who holds the appearance record for Aberdeen F.C.?
5. Which town has been both English and Scottish?
6. Of what type of stone is the Stone of Scone made?
7. What nationality was the prolific builder of Scottish roads, General Wade?
8. Why are the Football Club Airdrieonians nicknamed 'The Diamonds'?
9. Who wrote the popular epic poem 'Sir William Wallace'?
10. By what other name is the A9 road known?
11. Who is Arbroath's record goalscorer?
12. Where was reputedly Scotland's oldest coal mine located?
13. Which Scottish canal is 60.5 miles long?
14. What caused the population of Thurso to explode from 3,250 to 9,000?
15. In shipping terms what were the Queen Margaret Robert the Bruce, Mary Queen of Scots and Sir William Wallace?
16. Between which two Firths does Black Isle lie?
17. Which famous Scottish School was founded by Kurt Hahn?
18. In which Scottish City was Sir Arthur Conan Doyle born in 1859?
19. In which town is the Beltane Festival held?
20. Which playing card is known as 'The Curse of Scotland?

PICTURE QUIZ

41. To whom is this a memorial?

42. Name this athlete?

43. Name this castle?

44. A _____ cake?

45. Name this group?

(f) Name the tartan?

46. She appeared in "Local Hero".
Who is she?

THE MACALLAN GREAT SCOTS QUIZ

Quiz 53

1. How many times have Celtic won the Scottish Premier/1st Division up to 1990?
2. Where is Alexander III's Memorial?
3. By what name is An Claidh Mor more generally known?
4. Where are the famous Caithness Glass Works?
5. In which year did Edinburgh become Scotland's capital?
6. Where was the first North Sea oil terminal built?
7. What is the 'Old Man of Hoy'?
8. Which player holds the appearance record for Celtic?
9. Who had a hit record entitled 'Get It Right Next Time'?
10. Which poet was known as the Ettrick Shepherd?
11. When was the last time Scotland failed to qualify for the World Cup Finals?
12. What is the Grey Mares Tail?
13. Which Scottish steelworks was threatened with closure in May 1990?
14. What happened at Gretna in May 1915?
15. Which monarch was imprisoned at Lochleven in 1567?
16. Where in Scotland is the smallest professional theatre in the world?
17. What is the nickname of Aberdeen F.C.?
18. Who managed Manchester United to victory in the 1990 English F.A. Cup Final?
19. Where was the first purpose built Army Barracks in Britain?
20. Which town stands on the confluence of the rivers Tweed and Teviot?

Quiz 54

1. Which Bay lies between the Mull of Galloway and Burrow Head?
2. By what name was Malcolm IV better known?
3. How many times have Stirling Albion won the Scottish League Cup?
4. Who was the first pop artist in the history of the U.S. Charts to achieve Top 5 Hits in the Pop, Country, R. & B, Dance and Adult Contemporary Charts?
5. On which island will you find Drumadoon Point?
6. Who is the lead singer with Talking Heads?
7. Which two Islands are separated by the Kilbrannan Sound?
8. Which Scottish Football International transferred from Aberdeen to Spurs in 1980 for £800,000?
9. Which Composer of Reels and Strathspeys lived in Little Dunkeld?
10. Of what did Robert the Bruce allegedly die?
11. Which famous Scottish Bridge celebrates its centenary in 1990?
12. What does the Honourable Company of Edinburgh Golfers claim to be?
13. Which famous 007 was born in Edinburgh in 1930?
14. What was unique about the 1990 Scottish F.A. Cup Final?
15. Which Scottish Football Club are nicknamed The Diamonds and The Waysiders?
16. What does Eilean nan Righ mean in Gaelic?
17. What is the official road number of the road which skirts the northern side of Loch Laggan?
18. According to local belief what will happen when the stone basin in the Kirkyard of Trumfran on Skye finally dries out?
19. Which great Liberal Prime Minister had his home at Belmont?
20. Where will you find Loch Snizort?

THE MACALLAN GREAT SCOTS QUIZ

Quiz 55

1. In which publication will you find Oor Wullie?
2. Which author wrote 'The Little Minister'?
3. Which religious book became known as John Knox's Liturgy?
4. Which Scotsman founded the very first National park at Yosemite in 1864?
5. What was previously on the site of Princes Street Gardens in Edinburgh?
6. What is the name of the very tall skinny son in The Broons?
7. Which Scottish Football Club play at Starks park?
8. On which TV show did Wet Wet Wet make their TV debut?
9. What is the name of the village in Dumfrieshire founded by the Forestry Commission in 1947?
10. By what name is the A832 also known?
11. Which Gardens near Ullapool were abandoned in 1945 and rediscovered in 1985?
12. For which Bond Movie did Lulu sing the theme song?
13. In which year did Scotland join the United Kingdom of Great Britain?
14. What was first used in Scotland at Whittingehome East Lothian in 1932?
15. Which Scottish Football Club play in Royal blue shirts with an amber chest band?
16. Who scored Celtic's winning goal in the 1967 European Cup Final?
17. With which colleague from Paisley did Gerry Rafferty form the band 'Stealer's Wheel'?
18. For what invention was John Napier renowned?
19. In which year were the Five Articles of Perth: 1581; 1618 or 1718?
20. On which Communards single does Jimmi Somerville duet with Sarah-Jayne Morris?

Quiz 56

1. What was the alternative title of the Novel Peter Pan?
2. Against which side did Hibernian record their record victory of 22–1 in 1881?
3. What are Celtic F.C.'s colours?
4. What were 'Watchhouses' used for in Scottish Graveyards?
5. What is the name of the good looking daughter in The Broons?
6. Which double glazing company sponsor Glasgow Rangers?
7. What is the name given to the circular, cavity walled Towers prevalent in the Orkneys, Shetland Caithness and Sutherland?
8. What was the old Scottish measurement of 38" called?
9. At the end of which season was the Scottish Football League restructured into three divisions?
10. For which Scottish Football Club does Mixu Paatelainen play?
11. What was the population of Scotland according to Webster's Census of 1755: 520,621; 1,265,380 or 2,031,408?
12. Who wrote 'The Brigs of Ayr'?
13. What food is traditionally piped in at a Burns Night gathering?
14. Which town has golf courses at Darley, Lochgreen and Fullerton?
15. Who were Scotland's opponents on the night Jock Stein died of a heart attack?
16. Which company produced the first motor car in Scotland?
17. What in Scotland is a Clarsach?
18. Which castle was featured in 'Tarzan Lord of the Apes'?
19. What was the name of the Roman Road over the Cheviots which linked Soutra to Crammond?
20. Which French actor played the leading role in the film 'Highlander'?

THE MACALLAN GREAT SCOTS QUIZ

Quiz 57

1. Of which Scottish League Football Club was Peter Cormack Assistant manager in 1989-90?
2. What did Bass Rock become on the night of December 1st, 1901?
3. Where did the German High Seas Fleet surrender after the First World War?
4. Whose cottage in Largo is marked by his statue?
5. Which Scotsman was hailed as the 'Father of the United States Navy'?
6. At which battle was Sir Andrew Du Moray, First Lieutenant of William Wallace killed?
7. Which group had a No. 6 Hit with the song Radancer?
8. Where was the writer Thomas Carlyle born?
9. Who was the player involved in Meadowbank Thistle's record outgoing transfer?
10. After what is Portobello in Edinburgh reputedly named?
11. Which Scottish Football Club play at Links park?
12. Who was the manager of Rangers prior to Graeme Souness?
13. On which Beatles album does 'Ob La Di Ob La Da' by Marmalade feature?
14. How old was David I's successor Malcolm I?
15. Where was Rod Stewart born?
16. Which Scots guitarist learned to play guitar alongside Robert Fripp?
17. Who was also known as The Toom Tabard or Empty Coat?
18. Which star of Channel 4's 'Whose Line Is It Anyway' is from Largs?
19. Where did Beatrix Potter 'See' 'The Adventures of Peter Rabbit'?
20. Which famous island lies at the western tip of the Ross of Mull?

Quiz 58

1. Who scored the winning goal in the 1973 English F.A. Cup Final?
2. Which Celtic player has the current nickname of Jacki?
3. Which Cricket County knocked Scotland out of the 1990 Benson & Hedges Cup?
4. What are Louping-on-Stanes?
5. Where are the only two remaining Round Towers in Scotland?
6. What stretch of water lies between Nairn and Cromarty?
7. Who scored Brazil's opening goal when they defeated Scotland 4—1 in the 1982 World Cup Finals?
8. From Aviemore to where does the Strathspey Railway run?
9. What is the Scottish equivalent of an English Pigeon House?
10. Which Scottish Football Club play at Cappielaw Park?
11. Which Scottish City is known as Scotland's Dallas?
12. Which village featured in the film 'Local Hero'?
13. Finnan Haddies are used to make which Scottish soup?
14. What is the name of Annie Lennox's partner in Eurythmics?
15. Which government post is held by Malcolm Rifkind?
16. Where would you find Vaternish Point?
17. Why was the Equestrian Statue of Robert the Bruce erected at Bannockburn in 1964?
18. Which singer born in Bellshill in 1959 graduated as a teacher in Speech and Drama from the Royal Scottish Academy of Music?
19. In which film did Billy Connolly co-star with Michael Caine?
20. Who scored Scotland's opening goal in the 1978 World Cup Finals in Argentina?

THE MACALLAN GREAT SCOTS QUIZ

Quiz 59

1. For which Scottish League Football Club does Brian Ahern hold the appearance record?
2. Which group had a No. 2 Hit in 1985 with 'Kayleigh'?
3. Which Scottish Football Club are nicknamed 'The Bankies'?
4. On which Island would you find Calgary Bay?
5. What was a Halfpenny called in Scotland?
6. Which famous Scotsman was married to Jean Armour?
7. Which Scottish regiment were known as 'The Bubbly Jocks'?
8. What was the motto on Earl Marischals Standard at the Battle of Flodden Field?
9. Which singer had a No. 9 Hit in 1968 with 'I'm A Tiger'?
10. From which castle did James V escape the custody of the Douglases?
11. Which actor played the part of Scotty in Star Trek?
12. Which two families fought a pitched battle on the streets of Edinburgh in 1526?
13. Who was the manager of Celtic when they won the European Cup in 1967?
14. In which year was the Edinburgh Festival first held?
15. Which actor played the part of Hudson in 'Upstairs Downstairs'?
16. At which Palace did James V die?
17. Which group sang the original version of Lulu's 'Shout'?
18. On which Loch is St. Serf's Island?
19. How long is the River Tweed: 47; 97; 127 miles?
20. What are Solicitors called in Scotland?

Quiz 60

1. With which group does Neil Mitchell play keyboards?
2. Where are the Islands of Inchmurrin and Inchlonaig?
3. Who concluded the Alliance with France that became known as the 'Auld Alliance'?
4. Which Scottish Football Club are nicknamed 'The Ton'?
5. On which river does the town of Alloa stand?
6. Who was the singer with 'The Sweet'?
7. How many times did Aberdeen win the Scottish Cup in the 1980's?
8. Where was former Aberdeen manager Alex Ferguson born?
9. Which Monarch was defeated at the Battle of the Standard?
10. Which two islands lie between the Sound of Eigg?
11. Who succeeded William the Lion in 1214?
12. Who burned Dunkeld Cathedral in 1689?
13. Which island lies due west of Girvan on Scotland's West Coast?
14. What happened at Scone on Palm Sunday 1306?
15. Who had a hit with a song entitled 'Sweet Illusion'?
16. Which pop group were formerly known as The Gaylords?
17. Which Abbey in Berwickshire was founded in 1150 and was granted a Charter by David I?
18. Who replaced Alex Ferguson as manager of Aberdeen F.C.?
19. Which Scottish Football Club play their home matches at Stair Park?
20. Which famous West Indian cricketer played for Scotland in the 1990 Benson & Hedges Trophy?

THE MACALLAN GREAT SCOTS QUIZ

Quiz 61

1. Where was Irish Soccer International, Ray Houghton, born?
2. Which Auditorium was presented to the people of Dundee by Sir James Caird?
3. Which Scottish Author wrote 'The Adventures of Roderick Random'?
4. What is the most Northerly Town on the Scottish Mainland?
5. Which Scottish Football Club's Colours are Gold Shirts with a White Chest band?
6. Who founded The Boys Brigade Movement?
7. Why was Sheena Easton's '9 To 5' released as 'Morning Train' in the United States?
8. Who did Thomas Telford refer to affectionately as 'The Steam Engine Man from Glasgow'?
9. Who wrote the book 'Drove Roads of Scotland'?
10. Besides Sweden and Brazil who else comprised Scotland's Qualifying Group in Italia 90?
11. On which Island will you find Kiloran Bay?
12. Who had a Hit with the song 'Ole Ola (Muhler Brasiliera)?
13. In which Comic Strip does the character 'Fat Boab' appear?
14. Why did King James VI give the Lytes Jewel to Thomas Lyte?
15. Who did Mary Queen of Scots marry in 1558 aged 16?
16. Which now demolished Castle was once occupied by the Earls of Errol, Hereditary High Constables of Scotland?
17. Which Footballer was transferred from Celtic to West Ham in July 1988?
18. Who wrote the Soundtrack for the Film 'Local Hero'?
19. Who scored two goals for Rangers in the Skol Cup Final in October 1988?
20. What is the name of the subterranean passage near Troup Head which terminates in a large Cavern called 'The Devil's Dining Room'?

Quiz 62

1. Which Scottish football Club play at Easter Road?
2. The site of the seat of which Scottish Family is occupied by Thurso castle?
3. Which Grammy Award did Sheena Easton win in 1982?
4. What was read for the first time at St Giles in 1637 and caused riots?
5. What is 'Oor Wullie's favourite seat?
6. Who produced The Proclaimer's, 'Letter From America'?
7. With which Industry do you associate the Magnate, William Cunninghame?
8. From which Port do Fishing Vessels marked with BCK originate?
9. Which is the highest of the Six Peaks of Bennachie?
10. What was the name of the Family in 'Peter Pan'?
11. Who wrote 'The Nigger Question' in 1853?
12. Which D.I.Y. Chain sponsored the Scottish Football League?
13. Which Pop Singer was jeered when she appeared at Glasgow's Big Day Charity Show in 1990?
14. Which Newspaper became the voice of the Free Church after the disruption in Scotland?
15. What is the maximum number of points any one club can achieve in a Season in the Scottish Premier Division?
16. Who founded 'The New York Herald'?
17. Who scored Leeds United's only goal in the 1965 F.A. Cup Final?
18. What at 110 miles long is Scotland's Third Longest River?
19. Where in 1778 was the first successful Scottish Cotton Mill opened?
20. Which Clan had the War Cry 'Stand Fast Craigellachie'?

THE MACALLAN GREAT SCOTS QUIZ

Quiz 63

1. Which Secretary and favourite of Mary Queen of Scots was murdered at Holyrood Palace in 1566?
2. What are the Christian names of Gallagher & Lyle?
3. Who was the Thane of Cawdor?
4. Who gave his name to the process of dissolving rubber used to give Fabrics their waterproof coating?
5. Who wrote the novel 'Treasure Island'?
6. Where on Scotland's West Coast will you find the 'World In Miniature' Exhibition?
7. Who was the first woman to be presented with the 'Freedom of Wick'?
8. On which Island does the Annual Goatfell Race take place?
9. What is the name of the Thomas Telford designed bridge over the River Dee, 1.75 miles North of Kirkcudbright?
10. What type of Regiment were the Royal Scots Greys?
11. Who designed the Main Section of the Forth Bridge and received a Knighthood for his efforts?
12. Where did Robert the Bruce order his friend Sir James Douglas to bury his heart after his death?
13. Which 17 year old famous Scotsman was sent to Kirkoswald in 1775 to improve his Mathematics?
14. Who was sentenced to 14 years Transportation by Lord Broxfield for the crime of urging reform of Parliament and extension of the Franchise?
15. How many miles is Edinburgh from London: 705, 245, 405?
16. Who was relegated from the Scottish Premier Division after the 1988-89 Season?
17. Of which Electrical Group do Yarrow Shipbuilders form part?
18. Where did the 1990 Final of 'Mastermind' take place?
19. Who wrote the James Bond novels?
20. Which Heavy Metal Group was co-founded by Angus and Malcolm Young of Glasgow?

THE MACALLAN GREAT SCOTCH QUIZ

1. Can Scotch Whisky be made anywhere else in the world?
2. Which country is the leading importer of Scotch Whisky?
3. In what year was the Macallan Distillery licensed? 1724, 1824 or 1924
4. Which European country is the leading importer of Scotch Whisky?
5. What is a Single Whisky?
6. What is the Patent Still sometimes known as?
7. What is the residue in a Spirit Still known as after the distillation of the foreshots, potable spirits and feints?
8. Upon which river is the Macallan Distillery situated?
9. How many bottles of Scotch Whisky would you need to obtain 1 litre of pure alcohol?
10. Lowland Malt Whiskies are made south of an imaginary line drawn from where to where?
11. What is the main difference in the distilling of Scotch and Irish Whiskies?
12. In what year was the first reference to a distillery in the Acts of the Scottish Parliament? 1590, 1690 or 1790.
13. What type of casks do Macallan use for maturation?
14. According to law how old should a whisky be?
15. What are the 3 main ingredients of Scotch Whisky?
16. Does Scotch Whisky lose strength with age?
17. How long are Malt Whiskies usually matured for?
18. What gives some Scotch Whiskies a "smoky" flavour?
19. What ages of The Macallan are available in U.K. domestic market?
20. What accounts for between 75% and 80% of the price of a bottle of Scotch Whisky?
21. What is the liquid content of a bottle most commonly used for Scotch Whisky sales in the U.K.?
22. What was Clark's Hydrometer used for ?
23. What are the 2 main types of Scotch Whisky?
24. When was The Macallan Single Malt Whisky marketed in bottle's throughout the U.K? 1960, 1970 or 1980
25. By what method is Grain Whisky made?
26. Malt Whisky is usually classified in four main categories, what are they?
27. Macallan are sponsors of which cricket league?
28. What strength is most Scotch Whisky to be sold in the U.K.? 30%, 40% or 50%
29. At what temperature is whisky usually served in the U.K.?
30. On the 22nd of June, 1988, the Rotary Club of Elgin sold a 60 year old bottle of The Macallan to Sheraton Caltrust of Glasgow for a large sum of money making it the most expensive bottle of spirit — according to the Guiness Book of Records. Was it £4,000, £5,000 or £6,000?

(ANSWERS p.55)

THE MACALLAN GREAT SCOTS QUIZ

Quiz 64

1. How many Racecourses are there in Scotland?
2. Where is the Scottish Fisheries Museum?
3. What crossed the River Almond via the Almond Aqueduct?
4. Who invented the special type of pre-heated Furnace known as the 'Hot Blast' Process?
5. Who scored Scotland's Opening Goal of the 1990 World Cup Finals?
6. Which was the first UK Single to sell more than 2 million copies?
7. What was the venue for the 1990 Open Golf Championships?
8. Which Scotsman married Doctor Sarah Trevelyan in 1980?
9. Which Celtic Word means 'Fortified Hill'?
10. What did the U.K. Atomic Energy Authority take over to build the Dounreay Reactor?
11. Which Scottish Monarch died in 1460 when one of his own cannons exploded in his face?
12. Of which American Settlement was William Alexander, 1st Earl of Stirling, appointed Lieutenant in the 1620's?
13. Which Scottish Town derives its name from the Nordic 'Leir-Vik' meaning Clay Creek?
14. What marks the spot where Bonnie Prince Charlie raised the Jacobite Standard?
15. In which Town is the West Highland Museum?
16. How far is Glasgow to Edinburgh: 35, 40, 45?
17. Where in Scotland is Balhousie Castle and St Ninians Episcopal Cathedral?
18. With which sport would you associate Andrew Wood and Dougie Paterson?
19. What are Munro's in Scotland?
20. At which establishment is Gordon Stewart Head of Singing Opera?

Quiz 65

1. Over what distance is the Ayr Gold Cup run?
2. Where was Scottish Rugby International Sean Lineen born?
3. Which Glasgow Shoemaker opened the 'Quarriers Homes' for destitute children?
4. In which Comic Strip will you find 'Soapy Souter'?
5. What was the name of the horse ridden by Willie Carson to win the Oaks and St Leger in 1977?
6. Who writes the 'Paul On Pop' Column in 'The Sunday Post'?
7. What is the name of the popular Tourist Attraction near Loch Creran on Scotland's West Coast?
8. In which City were the infamous 'Gorbals'?
9. What is the Celtic word for river mouth or confluence?
10. Where is the famous 13ft long Cannon 'Mons Meg'?
11. What is the Gaelic Word which means 'The Black Headland'?
12. How far is the Lighthouse at the end of the Mull of Kintyre from the Coast of Ireland: 13, 33, 53 miles?
13. Of which Railway Branch Line was the Lochty Private railway once a part?
14. Who had a Hit Album in the 1970's entitled 'Ma'?
15. What type of weapons were associated with the Village of Doune near Stirling in the 17th and 18th Centuries?
16. On which Scottish River would you find Moncrieffe School and King James VI Golf Course?
17. What is the name of the Private company which owns Rosyth Dockyard?
18. Who had a No 3 Hit in 1974 with "Summerlove Sensation'?
19. What was the title of the official Glasgow Year of Culture Song?
20. Of which U.K. Company is Aberdeen born, Sir Denys Henderson, the Chairman?

THE MACALLAN GREAT SCOTS QUIZ

Quiz 66

1. Where is the Scottish Grand National run?
2. How many miles did Big Country mention in their hit song 'Fields of Fire'?
3. What was Duff House, designed by William Adam. used for between 1939-45?
4. Which Scottish League Football Club are nicknamed 'The Sons'?
5. Which Glasgow born Author wrote 'Mazurka'?
6. For which Scottish Rugby Union Side did Alan Tait play prior to switching to Rugby League?
7. Which famous British Actor, Producer, Director owns a farmhouse on the Island of Bute?
8. What material is Irn-Bru reputedly made from?
9. In which Village in the Scottish Borders will you find the Scottish Museum of Wool Textiles?
10. On an Island in which River is Threave Castle located?
11. What Monument contains the longest British Inscription in Runic Characters?
12. What is reputedly the most Northerly Castle in Britain?
13. Who had a No 3 Hit Album entitled 'All For a Song'?
14. Who scored Brazil's Goal in their 1-0 defeat of Scotland at Italia 90?
15. Where is the Scottish National War Museum located?
16. What is the nickname of the Scottish Football Club, Alloa?
17. With which Sport would you associate Andrew McQuistin?
18. What was the nickname of Lieut-Col Colin Mitchell former M.P. for West Aberdeenshire?
19. Which Scottish Football Club play their Home Matches at Palmerston Park?
20. In which film released in 1990 did Robbie Coltrane co-star with Eric Idle?

Quiz 67

1. Where is Edinburgh's Racecourse located?
2. For which Scottish Football Club did Blair Millar score 28 Goals in the 1978-79 Season?
3. Who co-wrote Tina Turner's, 'What's Love Got To Do With It' with Terry Britten?
4. What relative of the Princess of Wales lives on Seil Island on Scotland's West Coast?
5. Besides Jim Leighton and Brynn Gunn who was Scotland's other Goalkeeper in Italia 90?
6. With which Song did the Pipes and Drums and Military band of the Royal Scots Dragoon Guards reach No 13 in 1972?
7. What was the former name of the Castle of Mey?
8. Besides 'Bye Bye Baby' what was the Bay City Roller's only other UK No 1?
9. Which Monarch blew up Carnasserie Castle in Strathclyde after capturing it from the Duke of Argyll in 1685?
10. Where is the Agricultural Museum on Mainland Shetland situated?
11. Which famous Family's Home has been 'The Binns since 1612?
12. Which Sir Walter Scott Heroine reputedly lived in Curfew Row, Perth at the end of the 14th Century?
13. Which Waterway built in 1793 provides Fishing Boats with a short cut to the Atlantic avoiding a trip around the Mull of Kintyre?
14. Who was the first Explorer to reach the centre of the Continent of Australia?
15. In which year was the Glasgow & Garnkirk Railway opened: 1791, 1801, 1831?
16. In which Town will you find the Tam O'Shanter Museum and Dam Park Stadium?
17. For which Scottish League Football Club did Dan McDonald make a record 250 appearances?
18. Where are Royal Marine 45 Commando stationed in Scotland?
19. What is the name of the main character in John Buchan's 'The Thirty Nine Steps'?
20. On which Island will you find Kilchattan Bay and Port Bannatyre?

THE MACALLAN GREAT SCOTS QUIZ

Quiz 68

1. How many Scottish League Football Clubs play in the City of Edinburgh?
2. Which Character is played by Derek Lord in 'Take The High Road'?
3. With which Sporting Programme would you associate, Hazel Irvine?
4. In which Comic Strip would you find the character 'Wee Eck'?
5. Who is the Labour Party's Shadow Chancellor?
6. In which Scottish Town was Jockey, Willie Carson, born?
7. With which sport do you associate Jockey Wilson?
8. Which Guitarist/Vocalist was born on 10th October 1953 at Gambusland near Glasgow?
9. Which Country defeated Scotland 1-0 in their opening match of the 1990 World Cup Finals?
10. Which Company built the QE2?
11. Who co-commentates on 'Fight Night' with Reg Gutteridge?
12. Who was responsible for the first significant Art Nouveau Architecture in Great Britain?
13. Who wrote Books of Poems entitled 'Labrinth' and 'One Foot In Eden'?
14. On which Sea Loch will you find Strachur Bay?
15. Which great Inventor began his working life as an Instrument Maker for Glasgow University?
16. Which Castle was designed by Roger Morris and Roger Mylne in the style of a French Chateau?
17. Which Player holds the record for the greatest number of goals in a Season for Hibernian?
18. On whose Variety Show did Jimi Hendrix cause a sensation when he switched in mid-act to an unscheduled number?
19. On which Sea Loch does the Village of Sandbank lie?
20. Granton, Leith and Portobello are all areas of which City?

Quiz 69

1. What part is played in 'Emmerdale' by Frazer Hines?
2. Besides Rangers and Celtic which three other Clubs lie within the City Boundaries of Glasgow?
3. How many Scottish Infantry Regiments were still in existence in 1990?
4. What is the name of the Policeman in 'Oor Wullie'?
5. Who was elected as Member of Parliament for Moray in June 1987?
6. With which Sport do you associate Gillian Stewart?
7. How many times has Willie Carson won the Epsom Derby?
8. What unenviable Record did George McLean achieve on the A9 between Perth and Inverness?
9. Which Poet wrote 'Ne'er by the rivulets I strayed and ne'er upon my childhood weighed the silence of the Glens'?
10. For which Scottish Football Club did Donald Urquhart make 387 League Appearances?
11. In which year did the last of Glasgow's Tram Cars disappear?
12. Which Group formed by Gerry Rafferty and Joe Egan was conceived as a Scottish Version of 'Crosby Stills & Nash'?
13. Of which Organisation was James Jack formerly the General Secretary?
14. Which Edinburgh born Architect was responsible for the Piccadilly Hotel in London's West End?
15. Who was defeated by Alexander III at the Battle of Largs?
16. Who wrote 'The Princess and the Goblin' and 'The Princess and the Curdie'?
17. At the Southern end of which Island is Oronsay situated?
18. Which great Scottish Engineer began his life as a Stonemason?
19. Where is the 'Wall of the Seven Heads'?
20. With which Sport do you associate the name Peter Marinello?

THE MACALLAN GREAT SCOTS QUIZ

Quiz 70

1. Who wrote the Book 'The Shipbuilders'?
2. What song did Jim Watt sing after he won the World Lightweight Title at the Kelvin Hall?
3. From Port Elphinstone to where did Thomas Telford build a Canal in the 19th Century?
4. How many people comprise 'The Broon' Family?
5. Which Scottish football Club last won the Scottish F.A. Cup in 1893?
6. Which Group had a No 11 Hit in 1973 with 'This flight Tonight'?
7. At the time of the Union what was the approximate Population of Glasgow: 12,000 120,000 1,200,000?
8. Who wrote 'Journal of Our Life In The Highlands'?
9. In 1745 the Highlanders called it 'Bliadna Thearlaich'. What does it mean?
10. In which Park is the Braemar Gathering held?
11. Which Family own Braemar Castle?
12. Who played the part of 'Jamie' in Dr Who?
13. On which Island will you find Glen Varragill?
14. Which Rider won the 1990 Scottish Six Day Trial?
15. Which Cloth is identified by the symbol of an Orb?
16. Which Star of Radio 4 owns a 19th Century Home on the Isle of Skye?
17. Which Title did Dutchman, Rolf Muntz, win at Muirfield in 1990?
18. With which Sport would you associate Ivan Tukalo?
19. Where would you find the Kylerhea Otter Haven?
20. Of which Scottish Football Club is Wallace Mercer the Chairman?

Quiz 71

1. Where in Scotland would you have found the Forts Castlecary; Bar Hill; Kirkintilloch; Duntocher and Whitemoss?
2. Which Scottish Author wrote 'Shepherd's Calendar'?
3. With which Sport would you associate Rosemary Stirling?
4. Which is the Hometown of Rugby Club, Jedforest?
5. What does 'Lairig an Laoigh' mean?
6. What was the name of the Brewery which sponsored the Scottish Football League?
7. What is the Gaelic Word for Cup?
8. With which BBC 2 TV Comedy Series do you associate Gregor Fisher?
9. Who was known as 'The Black Colonel'?
10. What near Inverey is known as 'The Colonel's Bed'?
11. Which Scottish Football Club are nicknamed 'The Warriors'?
12. Which two people were mainly responsible for the 'Crofters Holding Act' of 1886?
13. Which famous Guitarist played with Al Stewart on his 'Love Chronicles' Album in 1969?
14. With what type of Industry would you associate John Brown & Co and Stephen of Linthouse?
15. What was the name of 'The Broon's Holiday Home?
16. What is the connection between The Wombles and the Isle of Mull?
17. What was jointly founded by R.B. Cunninghame Graham?
18. In which year did Fish leave the Group Marillion?
19. Against which Club did St Mirren achieve their Club record Victory in the Scottish Cup in 1960?
20. Which Scottish Football Club play in Navy Shirts with a white pinstripe on the front and a plain navy back?

A TALE OF A LUGGY BONNET

Keep this knot firmly tied

AN ANECDOTE related to us by our shooting acquaintances comes to mind. At the end of the day's sport, gamekeeper Jimmy Jamieson was observed waiting patiently among the party, his deerstalker's flaps *still tied across the top of his head,* his ears an exuberant blue with the Grampian cold.

"Why're ye standing in the wind with your bonnet not over your ears, Jimmy?" a friend inquired.

"I ha'na worn my bonnet since 'the disaster.'"

"What disaster, Jimmy?"

"The disaster when the Laird offered me a dram of The Macallan, and I didna hear him."

Such is the very stuff of Testimonials.

The Macallan. The Malt.

Picture Quiz

1. Tay Bridge
2. Annie Lennox
3. The Big Yin
4. Inverary Castle
5. The Wallace Monument
6. Schoolteacher
7. Mo Johnstone (first Catholic to play for Rangers)
8. Robbie Coltrane (Nuns On The Run)
9. The Forth Bridge
10. Marti Pellow
11. Dean Castle Kilmarnock
12. Hunterston "B" Nuclear Power Station
13. David Steel
14. Oban
15. Dundee United
16. Wet Wet Wet
17. Balmoral
18. Mitchell Library, Glasgow
19. Jimmy Boyle
20. Fish (of Merillion Fame)
21. Lulu
22. Steve Nicol (Footballer of the Year)
23. Gordan Brown, Labour spokesman for Trade and Industry
24. Pamela Stephenson (Billy Connolly)
25. Muriel Grey
26. Ayr
27. Holyrood
28. John Duncan Fergusson
29. Edinburgh Military Tattoo
30. The Lamont Harp or Clarsach
31. Gretna
32. Dumfries
33. Kinmount House
34. Frazer
35. Robert Burns
36. Sam Torrance
37. Robert Runcie
38. Royal Troon
39. Alexander Fleming
40. Eddie Reader (Fairground Attraction)
41. Robert Burns
42. Liz McColgan
43. Blair Castle
44. Dundee
45. Deacon Blue
46. Jenny Seagrove

Tartans:
(a) MacPherson
(b) Sinclair
(c) MacKenzie
(d) Scott
(e) Sutherland
(f) MacCallum

THE MACALLAN GREAT SCOTS QUIZ ANSWERS

Quiz 1

1. Ob La di-Ob La Da
2. The Lions of Lisbon
3. Nick Faldo
4. Theatre Royal, Glasgow
5. The Big Time
6. St. Columba
7. Rothesay Isle of Bute
8. David Livingstone
9. Inverary Castle
10. A82
11. Dunfermline
12. Roy Aitken
13. John Logie Baird
14. Kildrummy Castle
15. The Postage Stamp
16. St. Margarets Chapel
17. Four
18. David Steele
19. Tom Watson & Greg Norman
20. Thomas Telford

Quiz 2

1. The Burnetts of Ley
2. Average White Band
3. Powderhall Stadium
4. George Bruce
5. The Drummond Family
6. Colin Campbell of Glenorchy
7. Tarbolton
8. Prince of Wales
9. Ardmanurchan Peninsula
10. Alloway
11. Firth of Lorne & The Sound of Mull
12. Loch Katrine
13. Muriel Gray
14. August / September
15. Robbie Coltrane
16. Caledonia
17. Cubillas of Peru
18. Billy Connolly
19. Kenny Burns
20. John Laurie

Quiz 3

1. 1964
2. Scott Monument
3. Zaire
4. Mellenstain
5. The Proclaimers
6. 1812
7. Ben Nevis
8. The Adair of Kilhilt
9. Isle of Mull
10. Rothesay
11. 1759
12. Lomond
13. Glamis Castle
14. Souter Johnnies Cottage
15. Ardnamurchan Point
16. Dumbartonshire & Stirlingshire
17. Alexander I
18. Almond
19. James III
20. General Wade

Quiz 4

1. Earl of Strathmore
2. Claire Grogan
3. Duart Castle
4. Ben More
5. The Earl of Perth
6. To commemorate Charles I coronation as King of Scotland
7. Scotland World Cup Squad
8. Macbeth
9. Drummond
10. Edward I
11. William Smith
12. General Wade
13. Budian Ness
14. The Commando Memorial
15. Lorraine Kelly
16. Urquhart Castle
17. Neptunes Staircase
18. Loch Nan Uamh
19. David I
20. Loch Garten

Quiz 5

1. River Dee
2. St. Andrews
3. Tommy Gemmell
4. The Queen
5. George IV Bridge
6. Arbroath
7. Dr Jekyll and Mr Hyde
8. Victoria Dock, Dundee
9. Stuart Adamson
10. Dunkeld
11. Drumnadrochit
12. Shang-A-Lang
13. Ishmael Laguna
14. The McKenzies
15. European City of Culture
16. They were unbeaten
17. The Granite City
18. Burke and Haire
19. St. Andrews
20. Gleneagles

Quiz 6

1. John Gordon Sinclair
2. Alloway
3. Ayr
4. Prince Charles
5. 700ft.
6. Thomas Telford
7. Duke of Cumberland
8. 1890
9. 1542
10. Prince of Wales later Edward VII
11. Tobermory
12. 400 metres
13. 19 years
14. Sweet Dreams
15. Real Madrid
16. Donald Where's Your Troosers
17. Lecht
18. Seve Ballesteros
19. John Cobb
20. Mike Denness

THE MACALLAN GREAT SCOTS QUIZ ANSWERS

Quiz 7

1. Billy Connolly
2. Palace of Linlithgow
3. The Cuillins
4. Andy Stewart
5. Lewis
6. Fingal's Cave Overture
7. Jacobites/Hanoverians
8. Britain's First Nature Reserve in 1951
9. Inverewe Gardens
10. Shout
11. Tay Bridge Disaster
12. Bill Simpson
13. A Tourist
14. Aberdeen
15. Dundee
16. Kings College & Marischal College
17. 1190
18. Moira Anderson
19. Ian Charleson
20. Keep on Dancin'

Quiz 8

1. Craigevar Castle Aberdeenshire
2. International Festival
3. The Osprey
4. Inverness
5. Harris
6. Frankie Miller
7. Sgurr Alasdair
8. Cowgate Port
9. Ally McLeod
10. Inverness
11. Opportunity Knocks
12. Society dedicated to preservation of the Gaelic language
13. Faye Fife
14. Rugby Union
15. Macian
16. Middle of the Road
17. The Pap of Glencoe
18. Rangers
19. L'Heureux
20. Chrissie Hynde

Quiz 9

1. Bang Bang
2. The Three Sisters
3. Inter Milan
4. Kirkwall
5. Slik
6. Curling
7. Lerwick
8. Denis Law
9. Edinburgh
10. Stack Poly
11. Into The Valley
12. Loch Morar
13. Kenny Dalglish
14. George Street
15. Isle of Mull
16. Wet Wet Wet
17. The Forge
18. Alan Wells
19. Culloden
20. St. Magnus

Quiz 10

1. Shetland
2. Iran
3. David Bowie
4. The British Fisheries Society
5. Orkney Mainland
6. Lindsey McDonald
7. Dr. Fraser Darling
8. Zal Cleminson
9. Scalloway
10. China
11. Tom McKean
12. Suilvan
13. Duke of Argyll
14. Blue Peter
15. John Robertson
16. Holy Trinity Episcopal Church, Keith
17. Mary had a little lamb
18. Ardvreck Castle
19. 110 miles
20. Promised Your A Miracle

Quiz 11

1. Camperdown House
2. Lord Rockingham XI
3. James VI (later James I of England)
4. Charles II
5. Sir Thomas Bouch
6. St. Johnstoun
7. The Luvvers
8. Cameron Sharp
9. Firth of Clyde
10. Smeaton in 1771
11. Holyrood House
12. Nazareth
13. David Wilkie
14. Crannogs
15. George G. Parsonage
16. Fort William
17. Frederick Chopin
18. King Alexander III
19. He ran with only one shoe
20. Ullapool

Quiz 12

1. Midge Ure
2. River Nith
3. High Street
4. 27
5. Scone Castle
6. Every Picture Tells a Story
7. A Skye Terrier
8. Three Peaks Route
9. Culloden
10. Vienna
11. The Roach
12. Wanlockhead in Dumfries and Galloway
13. Wipper
14. Les McKeon
15. Duncryne Hill
16. Simpson Memorial Maternity Pavilion, Edinburgh
17. Its Coastline
18. The Powan or Freshwater Herring
19. Sutherland Brothers
20. Balmaha

THE MACALLAN GREAT SCOTS QUIZ ANSWERS

Quiz 13

1. Maggie Bell
2. Alexander Graham Bell
3. Arthurs Seat
4. Burt Lancaster
5. For Your Eyes Only
6. Lake of Menteith
7. Eaglais
8. Iain Cuthbertson
9. 1371
10. Maggie May
11. M8
12. The Royal Scots
13. Billy Connolly
14. Sir Walter Scott
15. Dunfermline Abbey
16. Loch Garten
17. Tunes of Glory
18. Andrew Carnegie
19. 1970
20. B.A. Robertson & Maggie Bell

Quiz 14

1. Boom Bang A Bang
2. Uniting the Picts & Scots
3. Bernard Gallagher
4. Charlie Endell
5. Rob Roy McGregor
6. Alexander Selkirk
7. Sir John Lyon
8. St Andrews University
9. Quiver
10. Loch Leven Castle
11. 1754
12. Bobby Moncur
13. Claire Grogan
14. Nigel Bruce
15. A74
16. J. M. Barrie
17. D.I.V.O.R.C.E.
18. Great Cumbrae
19. Frank McAvennie
20. The Borderers

Quiz 15

1. James III
2. McGuiness Flint
3. Loch Sloy
4. Sir Walter Scott
5. Tannochbrae
6. Kelvin Hall, Glasgow
7. Museum of Scottish Tartans
8. Balquidder
9. Archie Gemmill
10. HMS Unicorn-Dundee
11. Bay City Rollers
12. Cairngorms
13. 1 week
14. Colonel James Grant
15. Darnaway Castle
16. The Band of the Black Watch
17. David I
18. Drumnadrochit
19. Urquhart Castle
20. The Frazers of Lovatt

Quiz 16

1. Sir George Campbell
2. The Museum of Country Life
3. Dunolie Castle
4. Iona Cathedral
5. Wordsworth
6. Fish
7. Holytown, Lanarkshire
8. Calgary
9. Barbara Dickson
10. Horatio Nelson
11. Point of the Great Ocean
12. General Monk 1650
13. Ian Mc'Glagen
14. Billy Bremner
15. Kyle of Lochalsh
16. The element Strontium
17. Portree
18. Tommy Hutchinson
19. Eilean Donain
20. The Western Isles

Quiz 17

1. Yachting Regatta
2. Penny Ghael
3. Island of Iona
4. Arrochar
5. Charles Rennie McIntosh
6. Gare Loch
7. The Waverly
8. Ian McCafferty
9. Craignure
10. Aros Castle
11. New South Wales
12. The Crinan Canal
13. Lochgilphead
14. The Scots Baronial Style
15. Cromwell
16. McGuiness Flint
17. The Kingshouse Hotel, Strathclyde
18. Lismore
19. Kidnapped
20. The Red Fox

Quiz 18

1. With a Little help from My Friends
2. Firth of Clyde
3. The actor Edmund Keane
4. Dunoon
5. Father of Australia
6. Well of St. Mary
7. 1437
8. Richard II
9. David II
10. Ben More
11. Robert II
12. Organ Recitals
13. Museum of Transport
14. Don Masson
15. Demanded £15,000 and all the City's Arms
16. From the wreck of a Ship carrying earth from the Holy Land
17. Loch Eck
18. The Cobbler
19. St. Kessog
20. Kenneth McKellar

THE MACALLAN GREAT SCOTS QUIZ ANSWERS

Quiz 19

1. 1689
2. Deacon Blue
3. Earl of Gowrie
4. Henry Stuart
5. Solway Moss
6. James IV
7. Wet Wet Wet
8. James II
9. Garelochead
10. 1494
11. Margaret of Denmark
12. 1472
13. Provlands Lordship
14. William Wallace
15. The Comet
16. Henry Bell
17. Dunoon
18. Willie Johnston
19. Mary Campbell
20. Helensburgh

Quiz 20

1. Calve Island
2. Ulva Island
3. The Beatons
4. Bunesson
5. John O'Groats
6. St. Ignatius
7. Jimmy Page
8. Baxters
9. Forres
10. Caledonian Macbrayne
11. Alexander Earl of Buchan
12. Ireland
13. The Kilt
14. Lunan Bay
15. John Buchan
16. 1720
17. Chris Woods
18. Queen Anne
19. David Narey
20. Cromwell

Quiz 21

1. Liz McColgan
2. D. C. Thompson
3. Sulphur Springs
4. Gleneagles Hotel
5. Solway Firth
6. Berwick Rangers
7. Neil M. Gunn
8. Tayside
9. Deacon Blue
10. Dundee Utd.
11. Thurso
12. The Picts
13. 1954
14. Pentland Firth
15. Elizabeth 1st Countess of Sutherland
16. Kyle of Lochalsh
17. The Three Stacks of Duncansby
18. The Queen Mother
19. Wick
20. Dunnet Head

Quiz 22

1. Lord Mount Stephen
2. Glenlivet
3. Tomintool
4. Castle Grant
5. Graeme Souness
6. Edward I
7. St. John Ogilvie
8. The Marquis of Huntly
9. Ceylon
10. Macbeth
11. A9
12. The Lovat Scouts
13. Chiefs of the Clan Chisholm
14. Earl of Cromartie
15. Suilven
16. River Glass
17. Dingwall
18. Kenny Dalglish
19. Firth of Tay
20. Dundee

Quiz 23

1. 1715
2. Alan Rough
3. John Knox
4. James IV
5. James Watt
6. Regensburg, Bavaria
7. David Sole
8. 1513
9. Cults near Aberdeen
10. Drum Castle
11. Banff
12. 200ft high Cliffs
13. Ramsey McDonald
14. Abbotsford
15. Lady Hill, Elgin
16. St. Fergus
17. Inverugie Castle
18. Dracula
19. James Duff, 4th Earl of Fife
20. Edvard Grieg

Quiz 24

1. 1451
2. Tree Fossils
3. Kirkpatrick Macmillan
4. The roof collapsed due to the use of heavy stones
5. Sandback-Holy Loch
6. Glenbranter Forest
7. King Hakon of Norway
8. Loch Lomond
9. Luss
10. Robert Fleck
11. The Ardno Cairn
12. Strone Gardens Cairndow
13. Sheena Easton
14. Glen Croe & Glen Kinglass
15. Robert I
16. Bath
17. Robert Bruce
18. 1320
19. The Sovereign Status of Scotland
20. 1707

THE MACALLAN GREAT SCOTS QUIZ ANSWERS

Quiz 25

1. Braemar
2. Lecht Road
3. Kildrummy Castle
4. Alford
5. Deacon Blue
6. Earl of Dalhousie
7. Smoked haddock
8. Berwick Rangers
9. Brig O Balgourie Aberdeen
10. Kirriemuir
11. Bay City Rollers
12. Bon Accord
13. St. Ternan
14. Signing of Scottish Independence
15. Aberdeen
16. Aboyne Highland Games
17. Slim Jim
18. To preserve Balmoral's seclusion
19. Eleven
20. Barbara Mullen

Quiz 26.

1. Marmalade
2. River of the Caves
3. McLeods of Lewis & the Mackays
4. Dingwall
5. Omdurman
6. Struy Bridge
7. John Chisholm
8. Strath, Urquhart, Affric & Cannich
9. First Sheep Farm
10. Crusader
11. 4th Duke of Gordon
12. Bay City Rollers
13. Andy Roxburgh
14. Donald Mitchell
15. The Rose Family
16. Lossiemouth
17. Banff
18. Roman Catholic Priests
19. Dalriada
20. Banff

Quiz 27

1. Scone
2. Thomas Telford
3. 18th Century Iron Smelting Centre
4. McLaigs Folly
5. Ballachulish
6. Barbara Dickson
7. Deep Fjord
8. Seven Men of Moidart
9. The Disruption
10. William III
11. Edinburgh
12. Barragil Castle
13. Caithness Flagstones
14. Dundee
15. 1st Duke of Sutherland
16. Neil M. Gunn
17. Gleneagles
18. The Terrors
19. 10 Glebe Street
20. McDonalds & McLeods

Quiz 28

1. 111
2. Salvador Dali
3. 1964
4. His Son killed in World War 1
5. Shipping
6. Frank McAvennie
7. The People's Palace, Glasgow Green
8. Dunfermline
9. 1841
10. Cowal Highland Gathering
11. Pollockshaw Road
12. By Roasting Cats
13. Salen Village
14. Lachlan McQuarrie
15. Kilmartin Churchyard
16. Stone of Destiny
17. Mark McGhee
18. 15
19. Madeleine of France
20. John Jeffrey

Quiz 29

1. The 1588 wreck of 'The Florida'
2. Crofting on the Island
3. James of the Glens
4. The burial ground of the McKenzies
5. Big Country
6. John Bright
7. Nairn
8. Hanoverian
9. Deveron
10. Lochindorb
11. Paris
12. Robert Burns
13. William Ramsey
14. Queen's Park
15. 8
16. The Blue Bells of Scotland
17. Scotland The Brave
18. Altered Images
19. Bank of Montreal
20. Sir Walter Scott

Quiz 30

1. Mary Queen of Scots
2. The Satellite
3. Edward I
4. Sir Giles Scott
5. John Barbour
6. Stewarts of Appin
7. Fort William
8. William Wallace
9. Average White Band
10. Dunvegan Castle, Skye
11. Gavin Maxwell
12. David II
13. Clay Pigeon Shooting
14. 1425
15. The 6th Earl of Douglas & his Brother
16. Simple Minds
17. Anne of Denmark
18. Aztec Camera
19. Blind Harry
20. James III

The Macallan Great Scotch Quiz

1. No. Scotch Whisky must be wholly distilled and matured in Scotland
2. U.S.A.
3. 1824
4. France
5. The product of one particular distillery which has not been blended
6. The Coffey Still
7. Spent lees
8. River Spey
9. 3.1 bottles
10. Dundee in the east to Greenock in the west
11. Irish Whiskey distillers tend to favour 3 distillations rather than two in Scotland
12. 1690
13. Sherry casks
14. 3 years old
15. Cereals, water and yeast
16. No. Once bottled it never loses its strength
17. Up to 15 years
18. The peat fires over which the green malt is dried
19. 10, 18 and 25 years old
20. Tax
21. 75cl
22. To measure the strength of Scotch Whisky
23. Malt Whisky and Grain Whisky
24. 1980
25. The Patent Still method
26. Highland, Lowland, Campbelltown and Islay
27. North of Scotland Cricket League
28. 40%
29. Room temperature
30. £6,000

Scotch snap.

A manuscript from a Conservatoire of Music

Sirs, it may have come to your notice that in music we have a term _'Scotch Snap'._ This usually takes the form of a semiquaver followed by a dotted quaver, a device favoured particularly by baroque composers such as Handel giving a distinctive 'jerky' character to a dance tune.

It has been suggested in the Professors' Common Room that this figure derived its name from the rough liquors of the time which imparted _a sudden jolt to the Scottish tastebuds._

Today, of course, we have The Macallan Single Highland Malt Whisky, which provides such a delectable legato that the _Scotch_ snap has become quite forgotten – except of course in those bars where only baser spirits are jiggered out (in which case, may we suggest a _bar's rest?_)

Yours etc., Ian Curror,

FRCO (CHM), GRSM, ARCM, LRAM _and_ BAR.

The Macallan. The Malt.

THE MACALLAN GREAT SCOTS QUIZ ANSWERS

Quiz 31

1. St Moluag
2. Davy Provan
3. The Jesus and Mary Chain
4. Dornoch Firth
5. Macbeth
6. Alloa
7. Fish
8. Mull
9. St Margaret
10. Brechin City
11. Baker Street
12. Gourock
13. King David I
14. Both are called Annfield
15. Bay City Rollers
16. In Ain't Necessarily So
17. Thomas Telford
18. Annan
19. Murrayfield Racers
20. Tiree & Coll

Quiz 32

1. St Oran
2. Airdrieonians
3. Largs
4. Benbecula
5. Kenneth Mc'Alpin
6. 40
7. Marmalade
8. Loch Awe
9. To escape the Norman Conquest
10. Berwick Rangers
11. The Humblebums
12. Stranraer
13. King Magnus Barelegs of Norway
14. Clyde
15. Blair Drummond
16. Harold Melvin & The Bluenotes
17. Thomas Telford
18. Stirling Albion
19. Rhum
20. Waverley

Quiz 33

1. St Alban
2. Charlie Nicholas
3. Modern Girl
4. Cromarty Firth
5. Nectansmere
6. The Skol Cup
7. Sidney Poitier
8. Loch Fyne
9. Malcolm III
10. Ayr United
11. Gerry Rafferty
12. Because of his Eccentric Costume
13. Donald Ban
14. Billy McNeill
15. Stirling Castle
16. Rattlesnake
17. Bay City Rollers
18. 17 years
19. David Hume
20. Clyde

Quiz 34

1. 1959
2. Lloyd Cole & The Commotions
3. Battle of Arkinholm
4. St Andrew
5. Letter to Brezhnev
6. Gates Rubber company
7. Atmospheric Pollution
8. 1855
9. James Scott Skinner
10. Lockerbie
11. Steve Bronski & Larry Steinbachek
12. Alexander Stuart - Earl of Buchan
13. Dalriada
14. Crathes Castle
15. Average White Band
16. Kilmarnock
17. Under 16 World Cup
18. Bass Rock
19. Lulu
20. Solway Firth

Quiz 35

1. George Graham
2. For preferring a Mistress to his Wife
3. Bronski Beat
4. John Buchan
5. Brand New Friend
6. James IV
7. Aboyne Castle Grounds
8. Average White Band
9. Partick Thistle
10. Maurice Gibb
11. Ian St John
12. Isle of Skye
13. S.N.P.
14. James Barrie
15. Thomas Chalmers
16. James Keir Hardie
17. 1888
18. Motherwell
19. Jock Wallace
20. Antonine Wall

Quiz 36

1. Big Country
2. Edinburgh
3. Onnie Mc'Intyre
4. Granite
5. Glamis Castle
6. The Associates
7. Dounreay
8. Ian Mitchell
9. Strathspey Railway Company
10. Fort Augustus
11. Lloyd Cole & The Commotions
12. Royal Troon
13. Robbie Coltrane
14. Penicillin
15. Kilmarnock
16. Billy Connolly
17. Payne Stewart and Mark McNulty
18. Big Country
19. Caerlaverock
20. Saturday Night

THE MACALLAN GREAT SCOTS QUIZ ANSWERS

Quiz 37

1. Dunfermline
2. Every 100 years for a Day
3. Scapa Flow
4. Jimi Somerville
5. Grampian
6. Steve Ferrone
7. Prestwick
8. Edinburgh
9. Tam Paton
10. Largs
11. I Feel love
12. Bladnoch Malt Distillery, Wigtown
13. John Lawrie
14. A Mouse
15. 1940
16. R.L. Stevenson
17. Duke of Argyll
18. Altered Images
19. Bill Forsyth
20. Average White Band

Quiz 38

1. Fingal
2. The Rough Wooing
3. 8 Hours
4. 1426
5. The Associates
6. Ecosse
7. Kinmount House, Dumfriesshire
8. Eskdalelmuir
9. MacDonnell of Glengarry and the McKenzies of Kintail
10. Halidon Hill
11. Lloyd Cole & The Commotions
12. The Communards
13. Strath of Kildonan
14. Stones
15. Edinburgh
16. Peter Shilton & Ray Wilkins
17. Poisoning of the Earl & Countess of Sutherland
18. Dundee
19. Montrose
20. Big Country

Quiz 39

1. Bill Shankly
2. Bay City Rollers
3. A Halfpenny
4. Mull of Kintyre
5. Kerrerra Island
6. The McLeods
7. Nova Scotia
8. Annie Ross
9. Kidnapped
10. Edinburgh
11. Murrayfield
12. Aberdeen
13. 1st Duke of Sutherland
14. Scrabster
15. Fernitickles
16. The Rous Cup
17. The Flying Scotsman
18. Pit Ponies
19. Bronski Beat
20. Deepest lake in Britain

Quiz 40

1. Rangers & Celtic
2. Ireland
3. Hockenheim
4. She was acquitted in the famous Poisoning Trial
5. Former Pupils
6. Randwick
7. Meadowbank
8. David Balfour
9. Tommy Docherty
10. Scotch Eggs
11. Mary Queen of Scots
12. North Sea Oilfields
13. Black Agnes
14. Mashed Potato
15. A Young Child
16. Edinburgh
17. A Herring
18. Amazing Grace
19. Ten
20. Aztec Camera

Quiz 41

1. Half Woman - Half Serpent
2. Dundee
3. Hamilton
4. The Forth
5. Britain's Highest Golf Course
6. Alan McInally
7. Mary Queen of Scots
8. Darts
9. Mary Queen of Scots
10. Tommy Docherty
11. Mad Jocks and Englishmen
12. The Tweed
13. Holyrood House
14. Messenger took 62 Hours to reach Edinburgh
15. Clay Pigeon Shooting
16. Heroin Overdose
17. Aztec Camera
18. Four Seasons
19. They are both titles of Prince Charles
20. Lord Lion King of Arms

Quiz 42

1. General Dalyell
2. Bob Wilson
3. The Clyde
4. 16
5. The Orkneys
6. 3
7. Ben Johnson
8. Wick
9. 25th January
10. Fish Soup
11. Celtic Writing
12. Curling
13. Edinburgh Castle
14. Football
15. David Steel
16. Hermitage Castle
17. Stirling
18. Aberdeen
19. A Prison
20. A Turkey

THE MACALLAN GREAT SCOTS QUIZ ANSWERS

Quiz 43

1. Sanquhar nr Dumfries
2. Pick Up The Pieces
3. The Witches in Macbeth
4. Dundee
5. Mac The Scottie Dog
6. You Made Me believe In Magic
7. Edward Balliol
8. Annan & District
9. Dumfries
10. Martin Shaw
11. Altered Images
12. Jenny Seagrove
13. Dalbeattie Granite
14. Britain's narrowest Hotel
15. The Associates
16. Tweed
17. Annie Laurie
18. 750 ft
19. The Douglas fir
20. Robert Owen

Quiz 44

1. Robert Burns
2. Stone of Scone
3. Big Country
4. Craig Logan
5. Perfect
6. 1701
7. 1615
8. Willie Carson
9. 1503
10. Never Can Say Goodbye
11. 14th May 1943 in Glasgow
12. James II
13. William Dunbar
14. Arsenal
15. The Pretenders
16. Marquis of Queensberry
17. Sonido
18. Everton
19. Dumfries Academy
20. Dumfries

Quiz 45

1. Prince Charles
2. Robert Burns
3. Bishops of Moray
4. Marchere Marconi
5. Average White Band
6. By sticking a Pin in the Map of America
7. 1957
8. Richard Coles
9. Celtic
10. Serpentine Marble
11. Catholic Priests
12. ICI
13. Mark Brzezigi
14. The Cocteau Twins
15. Keir Hardie
16. Fairground Attraction
17. Muirfield
18. Maurice Johnston
19. Jim Milligan
20. Aston Villa

Quiz 46

1. The Old Grey Whistle Test
2. James Marhew
3. A Summer Hill Pasture for Cattle
4. Daphne
5. Duchess of York
6. Inverfolly National
7. Hibernian
8. Criffel
9. Dalbeattie
10. The Cheviots
11. Man City
12. Lulu
13. John Knox
14. Irish
15. The Ceildon HIlls
16. Stenhousemuir
17. Peter Pan
18. Kirkcudbright
19. The Water of Fleet
20. Wet Wet Wet

Quiz 47

1. John Loudon McAdam
2. Advocate
3. Kilts
4. Ian St. John
5. To locate the Loch Ness Monster
6. Horace
7. Headlands on the Black Isle
8. Burned at the Stake
9. Fish of Marillion
10. Leeds United
11. Lord Lieutenant of Morayshire
12. Dounreay
13. Ben Nevis
14. Richard the Lionheart
15. Craigenputtock
16. Whisky
17. The Arholl Highlanders
18. Stinking Billy
19. Pittodrie
20. The Americas Cup

Quiz 48

1. Procurator Fiscal
2. Bobby Kerr
3. Glasgow
4. The Duke of York
5. A gun in Edinburgh Castle
6. Windows for Lepers to watch Church services
7. The Forth Bridge
8. Highlander
9. Kintyre
10. Brude — King of the Picts
11. He used to wallow in his bath like a fish
12. Ronnie Simpson
13. A stone circle
14. Ellisland
15. Rev. J. Renwick
16. Thomas Telford
17. To House Pigeons
18. 1034
19. St. Mirren
20. £30,000

THE MACALLAN GREAT SCOTS QUIZ ANSWERS

Quiz 49

1. Cutty Sark
2. Hamburg
3. A Border Marauder
4. John Gray
5. Tommy Craig
6. Scottish National Flag
7. Gallagher and Lyle
8. Coigach
9. Granton to Burntisland
10. Dover House, Whitehall
11. Lesisian Gneiss
12. North Uist & Harris
13. Black Donald
14. The Great Michael
15. The Cromarty Firth
16. River Esk
17. Clyde
18. Never Say Never Again
19. Marillion
20. Royal Company of Archers

Quiz 50

1. 7–0 Uruguay 1954
2. Thomas Carlyle
3. Dumbarton
4. Scottish Silver Dollar
5. Fulton Mackay
6. Tottenham Hotspur
7. Cromarty Firth
8. A plot of land
9. Scapa Flow
10. Rome
11. Mark McGhee
12. Clydebank
13. 1984
14. Dumbarton
15. Scotland's First Printing Press
16. Peter Lorimer
17. A kilt
18. Detective Agency
19. Children
20. MacDonalds

Quiz 51

1. Queen of the South
2. Aberdeen
3. Yrhan
4. Crombie
5. Kenny Rogers
6. Talking Heads
7. Robert The Bruce
8. Firth of Forth
9. Meat & potato pastie
10. Al Stewart
11. Northants
12. A deep valley near Moffat
13. Both nicknamed Saints
14. Sunderland
15. Robert The Bruce
16. A cross between a Yak and a Highland cow
17. Manderston, Berwickshire
18. The wolf
19. Feyenoord
20. Carnegie

Quiz 52

1. Talking Heads
2. Crown of Ireland
3. Jim Leighton
4. Willie Miller
5. Berwick Upon Tweed
6. Red sandstone
7. Irish
8. They wear a diamond on their shirts
9. Blind Harry
10. Great North Road
11. Jimmy Jack
12. Brora, Sutherland
13. Caledonian Canal
14. Dounreay Power Station
15. Queensferry Ferries
16. Moray & Cromarty
17. Gordonstoun
18. Edinburgh
19. Peebles
20. Nine of diamonds

Quiz 53

1. 35 times
2. Kinghorn, Fife
3. The Claymore
4. Wick
5. 1124
6. Sullom Voe
7. A rock pinnacle in the Orkneys
8. Billy McNeill
9. Gerry Rafferty
10. James Hogg
11. 1970
12. Waterfall near Moffat
13. Ravenscraig
14. A railway disaster
15. Mary Queen of Scots
16. Dervaig, Mull
17. The Dons
18. Alex Ferguson
19. Berwick Upon Tweed
20. Kelso

Quiz 54

1. Luce Bay
2. Malcolm The Maiden
3. None
4. Sheena Easton
5. Arran
6. David Byrne
7. Arran & Kintyre
8. Steve Archibald
9. Neil Gow
10. Leprosy
11. The Forth Bridge
12. World's oldest golf club
13. Sean Connery
14. First penalty shoot-out
15. Airdrieonians
16. The Kings Isle
17. A86
18. The day of Judgement
19. Henry Campbell-Bannerman
20. Isle of Skye

THE MACALLAN GREAT SCOTS QUIZ ANSWERS

Quiz 55

1. The Sunday Post
2. J. M. Barrie
3. Book of Common Order
4. John Muir
5. Nor Loch
6. Hen Broon
7. Raith Rovers
8. The Tube
9. Ae
10. Destitution Road
11. Leckmelm Gardens
12. The Man With The Golden Gun
13. 1707
14. Combine harvester
15. Stanraer
16. Steve Chalmers
17. Joe Egan
18. Logarithms
19. 1618
20. Don't Leave me This Way

Quiz 56

1. The Boy Who Never Grew Up
2. 42nd Highlanders
3. Green and White Hoops
4. Used by sentries to stop bodysnatchers
5. Maggie
6. C. R. Smith
7. Brochs
8. An Ell
9. 1974-75
10. Dundee United
11. 1,265,380
12. Robbie Burns
13. Haggis
14. Troon
15. Wales
16. Argyll Motor Company Alexandra
17. A Harp
18. Floors Castle Kelso
19. Dere Street
20. Christopher Lambert

Quiz 57

1. Hibernian
2. A lighthouse
3. Firth of Forth
4. Alexander Selkirk
5. John Paul Jones
6. Stirling Bridge
7. Marmalade
8. Ecclefechan
9. Darren Jackson
10. Admiral Vernon's victory in 1739
11. Montrose
12. Jock Wallace
13. The White Album
14. Eleven
15. Highgate, London
16. Al Stewart
17. John Balliol
18. John Sessions
19. Mr. McGregors Garden
20. Iona

Quiz 58

1. Ian Porterfield
2. Dziekanowski
3. Leicestershire
4. Stairs for mounting horses
5. Brechin & Abernethy
6. Moray Firth
7. Zico
8. Boat of Garten
9. Doocot
10. Morton
11. Aberdeen
12. Pennan
13. Cullen Skink
14. Dave Stewart
15. Secretary of State for Scotland
16. Isle of Skye
17. To commemorate the 650th anniversary
18. Sheena Easton
19. Water
20. Joe Jordan

Quiz 59

1. Clyde
2. Marillion
3. Clydebank
4. Mull
5. Bawbee
6. Robbie Burns
7. Royal Scots Greys
8. Truth Prevails
9. Lulu
10. Stirling
11. James Doohan
12. Douglases & Hamiltons
13. Jock Stein
14. 1947
15. Gordon Jackson
16. Palace of Falkland
17. The Isley Brothers
18. Loch Leven
19. 97
20. Writers to the Signet

Quiz 60

1. Wet Wet Wet
2. Loch Lomond
3. William I
4. Morton
5. River Forth
6. Brian Connolly
7. Four Times
8. Govan, Glasgow
9. David I
10. Eigg & Muck
11. Alexander II
12. The Cameronians
13. Ailsa Craig
14. Robert Bruce was crowned King of the Scots
15. Junior Campbell
16. Marmalade
17. Dryburgh Abbey
18. Ian Porterfield
19. Stranraer
20. Gordon Greenidge

THE MACALLAN GREAT SCOTS QUIZ ANSWERS

Quiz 61

1. Glasgow
2. The Caird Hall
3. Tobias Smollett
4. Thurso
5. Dumbarton
6. Sir William Smith
7. Due to Dolly Parton's song from the film '9 To 5'
8. James Watt
9. A.R.B. Haldane
10. Costa Rica
11. Colonsay
12. Rod Stewart
13. Oor Wullie
14. For tracing the Genealogy of the Kings of Britain
15. The Dauphin Francois
16. Slains Castle
17. Allen McKnight
18. Mark Knopfler
19. Ally McCoist
20. The Needles Eye

Quiz 62

1. Hibernian
2. Sinclair
3. Best New Artist 1981
4. Revised Prayer Book for Scotland
5. A Bucket
6. Gerry Rafferty
7. Tobacco
8. Buckie
9. Oxen Craig
10. Darling
11. Thomas Carlyle
12. B & Q
13. Sheena Easton
14. The Witness
15. 72
16. James Gordon Bennett
17. Billy Bremner
18. The Spey
19. Rothesay
20. The Clan Grant

Quiz 63

1. David Rizzio
2. Benny & Graham
3. Macbeth
4. Charles Mackintosh
5. Robert Louis Stephenson
6. North Pier, Oban
7. The Queen Mother
8. Arran
9. Tongland Bridge
10. Cavalry Regiment
11. Benjamin Baker
12. Jerusalem
13. Robert Burns
14. Thomas Muir
15. 405
16. Hamilton Academicals
17. G.E.C.
18. Glasgow City Chambers
19. Ian Fleming
20. AC/DC

Quiz 64

1. Five
2. Anstruther
3. Edinburgh & Glasgow Union Canal
4. J.B. Neilson
5. Stuart McCall
6. Mull of Kintyre
7. St Andrews
8. Jimmy Boyle
9. Dun
10. Disused Royal Naval Air Station
11. James II
12. Nova Scotia
13. Lerwick
14. Glenfinnan Monument
15. Fort William
16. 45
17. Perth
18. Rally Driving
19. Peaks Over 3000ft
20. Royal Scottish Academy of Music & Drama

Quiz 65

1. Six Furlongs
2. New Zealand
3. William Quarrier
4. Oor Wullie
5. Dunfermline
6. Paul Coia
7. Sea Life Centre
8. Glasgow
9. Aber
10. Edinburgh
11. Rossdhu
12. 13 miles
13. East Fife Central Railway
14. Lena Zavaroni
15. Flintlock Pistols
16. River Tay
17. Babcock Thorn
18. Bay City Rollers
19. Stand Proud
20. I.C.I.

Quiz 66

1. Ayr
2. 400 miles
3. To House German P.O.W.'s
4. Dumbarton
5. Campbell Armstrong
6. Kelso
7. Sir Richard Attenborough
8. Girders
9. Walkerburn
10. River Dee
11. The Ruthwell Cross
12. Muness Castle, Shetlands
13. Barbara Dickson
14. Muller
15. Edinburgh Castle
16. The Wasps
17. Curling
18. Mad Mitch
19. Queen of the South
20. Nuns On The Run

THE MACALLAN GREAT SCOTS QUIZ ANSWERS

Quiz 67

1. Musselburgh
2. Clydebank
3. Graham Lyle
4. Frances Shand-Kydd
5. Andy Goram
6. Little Drummer Boy
7. Barrogill Castle
8. Give A Little Love
9. James II
10. Tingwall
11. The Dalyells
12. The Fair Maid of Perth
13. The Crinan Canal
14. John McDougall Stuart
15. 1831
16. Ayr
17. Stranraer
18. Arbroath
19. Richard Hannay
20. Isle of Bute

Quiz 68

1. Three
2. Sneddon
3. Scotsport
4. Oor Wullie
5. John Smith
6. Stirling
7. Darts
8. Midge Ure
9. Costa Rica
10. John Brown & Co
11. Jim Watt
12. Charles Rennie McIntosh
13. Edwin Muir
14. Loch Fyne
15. James Watt
16. Inverary Castle
17. Joe Baker
18. The Lulu Show
19. Holy Loch
20. Edinburgh

Quiz 69

1. Joe Sugden
2. Clyde, Partick & Queens Park
3. Seven
4. P.C. Murdock
5. Margaret Ewing
6. Golf
7. Three
8. Highest Recorded Speed on a Police Radar Trap
9. Alexander Smith
10. Raith Rovers
11. 1962
12. Stealers Wheel
13. Scottish T.U.C.
14. Richard Norman Shaw
15. Haakon, King of Norway
16. George McDonald
17. Colonsay
18. Thomas Telford
19. Invergarry
20. Football

Quiz 70

1. George Blake
2. Flower of Scotland
3. Aberdeen
4. Eleven
5. Queens Park
6. Nazareth
7. 12,000
8. Queen Victoria
9. Charlies Year
10. Princess Royal Park
11. The Farquharsons
12. Frazer Hines
13. Isle of Skye
14. Steve Saunders
15. Harris Tweed
16. Derek Cooper
17. Amateur Golf Championship
18. Rugby Union
19. Isle of Skye
20. Hearts

Quiz 71

1. Antonine Wall
2. Ian McPherson
3. Athletics
4. Jedburgh
5. Pass of the Calves
6. Drybrough's
7. Quoich
8. Naked Video
9. John Farquharson
10. Cave in a Gorge
11. Stenhousemuir
12. Lord Napier & the Duke of Argyll
13. Jimmy Page
14. Shipbuilding
15. The But an Ben
16. Tobermory
17. Scottish Council of Labour
18. 1988
19. Glasgow University
20. Raith Rovers